D1127103

THE FIFTEEN JOYS OF MARRIAGE

Translated from the French
by
ELISABETH ABBOTT

WITH ILLUSTRATIONS
BY RENÉ BEN SUSSAN

THE ORION PRESS - NEW YORK

Library of Congress Catalog Card Number: 59-13322
Manufactured in Italy by Stamperia Artistica Nazionale, Torino

PREFACE

This masterpiece of French medieval prose has remained anonymous for five and a half centuries. The mystery of the author's identity seemed insoluble until a manuscript of *The Fifteen Joys* was found by André Pottier in 1830 in the library of Rouen, a manuscript which terminated in this enigmatic octave and a note advising that this octave contains the name of the author:

De labelle la teste oustez
Tresvistement davant le monde
Et samere decapitez
Tantost et après le seconde
Toutes trois a messe vendront
Sans teste bien chantée et dicte
Le monde avec elles tendront
Sur deux piez qui le tout acquite.

En ces huyt lignes trouverez le nom de celui qui a dictes les XV joies de mariage au plaisir et à la louange des mariez. Esquelles ils sont bien aises. Dieu les y veille continuer.

Pottier believed that he could, by isolating certain syllables, decipher the name *Antoine Lasale* (Antoine de La Salle), the celebrated author of *Petit Jehan de Saintré*, and this identification was at first generally accepted.

Since then, however, there have been many other attempts to solve the riddle, and doubts have been cast upon the attribution to La Salle. Among the names proposed were *Sieur de Bellesme* and a certain *Lemonde* of Escé. Pierre Louÿs turned his attention to the cryptic lines and discovered the name of *l'Abbé de Samer*, whom he believed to be Pierre II, who was Abbot of Samer, a Benedictine abbey near Boulogne, about 1380. Then Alfred Coville identified the author with Gilles Bellemère, Bishop of Avignon from 1380 to 1390, who lived at the court of the antipope Benedict XIII. But many scholars have been unwilling to ascribe the trenchant humour of *The Fifteen Joys* to Bellemère, an author otherwise known only for treatises on canon law.

Unless further evidence is found, it seems unlikely that the author's name can be identified with certainty. However, it can be deduced from the style, text and certain historical allusions that the author took for his model the *Miroir de Mariage*, written by Eustache Deschamps about 1410-20. It also seems beyond doubt that the author, although singularly well informed about worldly passions, was a priest, and that he was practiced in juridical questions. He states in the Prologue that he was never married "*pour ce qu'il a pleu à Dieu me mettre en autre servage,*" but he offers us no more specific clues.

Of six gothic editions the oldest, which is undated, was probably printed in Lyons between 1480 and 1490. The popularity of this classic has never waned, although we have never learned to whom we owe the pleasure.

S. C.

CONTENTS

THE FIFTEEN JOYS OF MARRIAGE

PROLOGUE

Many men have sought to show, with much reasoning and authority, that man enjoys greater happiness on earth by living in freedom and liberty than by allowing himself to be enslaved of his own free will. In their opinion a man is not in his right senses who may enjoy the pleasures and delights of the world in the flower of his youth and, voluntarily and of his own initiative, seeks the entrance into a narrow, painful prison, full of tears, groans and lamentations and needlessly rushes into it. And once he is inside, the door, which is of iron and closes with great bars, is shut on him, and he is so closely confined that, despite all his prayers and entreaties, never shall he get out. Above all we would think a man mad and senseless to be thus imprisoned if he had heard the prisoners weeping and groaning in the prison beforehand.

And as human nature yearns for liberty and reason, many great lords have lost their estates, because those lords wished to rob their subjects of their liberty. Moreover many towns and cities and many humble folk have been destroyed through disobedience or a desire for too much liberty, for which many great wars have been waged and many men have died. Thus the French lords, by their great valour, were freed and exempted from tributes and servitude to the Emperors of Rome, whereby many battles have been fought and won on behalf of the French. And so it came about that when they were not strong enough to attack the great powers of the Emperor, who had invaded their land, they preferred to rise up and depart from their country rather than pay service tribute to the Emperor, whereby they showed the great nobility of their hearts. And so they went away, conquering lands and properties by their valour, and afterwards won back nobly at the point of the sword their land of France, which land they have kept free until now to their profit. And because the peoples of all nations that were enslaved wished to be in France that they might be free, it came to pass that France was the noblest land in the world, the richest, the most populated, the best builded, flourishing with wealth, with science, with law, with the Catholic faith and with all other virtues. And since they were free, it was reasonable that they should set their people free by giving law to the subjects they had taken to themselves. For it is not reasonable to have one law for oneself and another for one's neighbor. Wherefore it has come to pass that the land is deserted, empty of people, lacking in knowledge and in many other virtues. And in consequence sin and vice reign there, whereas in general every man should look to the public good.

We may say that, as a rule, he who does not look to his own good is not in his right senses, especially when he may do so without harming others; for he would be held to have little wit who would deliberately fling himself into a pit, wide at the bottom and narrow at the top, from which no man can get out. Such pits are dug to trap wild beasts in the forests. And wherever they have fallen into those pits they are greatly astonished and turn and twist to find a way out, but then it is too late.

The same may be said of those who are married, who are like a fish swimming in the great water, that is free to go to and fro as he pleases; and he thrashes about so much that at last he finds a fish trap in which there are a number of fish who have been caught by the bait inside which they have smelled out from the scent. And when that fish sees them, he works as hard as he can to get in and circles round and round the fish trap until at last he finds the way in, and he enters into it, thinking he is in all delights and pleasures even as he thinks the others are. And when he is there he cannot come out again and is in grief and sorrow there where he thought to find nothing but joy and delight. The same may also be said of those who are to marry, for they see other married men in the trap pretending to swim and to disport themselves, and they make such efforts that at last they find a way in. And when they are in they cannot find a way out, but are forced to remain there. So said a Doctor Valère to one of his friends who had married and who asked him if he had done well. And the doctor answered as follows:

"My friend," said he, "couldn't you find a high window from which you could have plunged head foremost into a deep river?" Meaning, of course, that a man should expose himself to the greatest dangers rather than lose his freedom. Greatly did the Archdeacon of Thérouenne repent that, to enter the state of marriage, he abandoned the noble privilege and estate of the clergy and married a widow to whom, as he relates, he long dwelt enslaved, in great grief and suffering. Repenting which, he composed a beautiful treatise to comfort himself and as a warning to others, and many other men have striven in many ways to show what suffering there is in marriage. And even as certain devout persons, thinking of the Virgin Mary and meditating upon the great joys she experienced during the holy mysteries of the Annunciation, the Nativity, the Ascension of Jesus

Christ, and others which they have set down in "Joys" in the name and for the honour of whom many good Catholics have made beautiful and devout orisons to the honor and praise of the blessed Virgin Mary, so I, too, musing upon and considering the state of marriage in which I never was (since it has pleased God to place me in another servitude, without freedom which I can nevermore recover), am of the opinion that in marriage there are fifteen ceremonies, according to what I have seen or heard from those who know it well. And those who have married consider them joys, delights and pleasures and think no other joys can be compared with them. But, according to the best understanding, those fifteen joys of marriage are, in my opinion, the greatest torments, sufferings, sorrows and the fifteen greatest woes in this world; and no other tortures, with the exception of breaking one's limbs, last so long. And yet I do not blame them for entering into matrimony, but am of their opinion and say they do well, for we are in this world solely to do penance, suffer afflictions and mortify the flesh in order to gain Paradise. And it seems to me that a man can do no sharper penance than to suffer and endure the great pains and great torments that are hereinafter set down and declared. One thing, however, comforts me; for those who are married consider those same pains and torments as joys and delights and are as hardened and accustomed to them as an ass is to bear burdens and they seem to rejoice in them; and for this we must doubt whether they will have any merit. Therefore, looking upon those pains which they mistake for joys and considering the contradiction between their judgement and mine as well as that of various others, I have taken delight, as I watch them drowning in the trap where they are so firmly caught, in describing those FIFTEEN JOYS OF MARRIAGE to console them, thereby wasting my pains, my ink and my paper. As to those who are unmarried and who will not fail to marry and enter the trap, I shall say nothing; though some of them perhaps may repent when it is too late. And therefore they shall dwell forever in those joys and will end their days miserably.

THE FIRST JOY

The first joy of marriage is when the young man is in the first flush of youth, when he is fresh, lively and merry and cares for nothing but to prove his prowess in love, compose ballads and sing them, ogle the prettiest wenches and consider where he may take his pleasure and delight according to his degree; and he has no care as to whence comes the money he has, for perhaps he still has father and mother or other kinsfolk who give him whatever he needs.

And though he has his ease and pleasure in abundance, he is not content, but gazes enviously at those who are married and firmly caught in the trap. And he sees them disporting themselves with delight — or so it seems to him — for they have the bait beside them in the trap, in other words, the woman, and she is beautiful, bedecked with jewels and finely apparelled in gowns which, perhaps, her husband has not paid for; for he is told that her father or mother gave them to her from their bountiful store. So the young man turns and turns about the trap and to such good purpose that at last he enters into it and is married. And so eager is he to snatch at the bait that he frequently gives little thought to the consequences and plunges in regardless of the cost.

Now he is in the trap, the poor man who was wont to concern himself solely with singing and with buying ribbons, silk purses and other charming baubles to give to pretty wenches. There, for a little while, he frisks about and enjoys himself and has no thought of escape, till one fine day he realizes what is happening, but it is too late. His wife must be set up in the estate befitting her. And perchance her heart is gay and merry, and at a feast the other day she saw the ladies and citizens' wives or other women of her estate who were garbed in the latest fashion. And she says to herself that it is indeed due to her house and kin that she should be as well dressed as others.

Then she waits for the suitable place, time and hour to speak of this matter to her husband; for women like to speak of their special matters there where their husbands are most subject and must needs be inclined to grant their wishes — that is, in bed where the fellow whereof I speak is thinking of this delight and pleasure and to him it seems he has nothing else to do.

Then his lady begins and speaks as follows:

" My dear, leave me alone for I am greatly distressed."

" My sweet," says he, " and wherefore ? "

" *Certes*," says she, " I have good reason to be, but I shall say nothing to you, for you heed not my words."

" My love," says he, " tell me why you speak so to me ? "

" *Par Dieu*, sir," says she, " there is no need to tell you: for if I told you, you would make light of it and you would deem I did it for another cause."

" Verily," says he, " you shall tell me."

Then she says:

" Since it pleases you, I will tell you, my dear," says she. " You know that the other day I was at such and such a feast where you sent me — quite against my wishes. But when I was there, I think there was no woman (no matter how lowly her estate) who was so poorly dressed as I. Though I say it not to praise myself, yet thanks be to God, I am as well born as any lady, demoiselle or merchant's wife there. I leave it to those who are skilled in noble descents. I say this not to glorify myself, for I care not how I am dressed; but I was ashamed for my love of you and of my kin."

" *Par Dieu!* " says he, " my love, and how were they dressed? "

" Faith! " says she, " There was none so lowly of my estate but had a gown of scarlet or malines or of fine green, furred with good grey or miniver, with large sleeves, a high-peeked hood to match, with a tissue of red or green silk, falling to the ground and all in the very latest style. And I still have only my wedding gown that is faded and very short, seeing that I have grown since it was made, for I was still but a child when I was given to you and already I am so worn and have endured so many woes that I look the mother of those whose daughter I could be. When I was among them I was so ashamed I knew not how to keep countenance nor dared put on a bold front. And it grieved me most when the lady of such a place and the wife of such an one told me before them all it was a great shame I was no better dressed. And, forsooth, it is long since they have been to see me.

"*Mon Dieu*, my sweet," said the goodman, "I will tell you something. You know well, my dear, that we are hard pressed and you also know, my dear, that when we entered upon housekeeping, we lacked all furnishings and needs must buy beds, bedding, room furnishings and many other things, and we have not much money at present. And you know well we must buy two oxen for our farmer in such a place. And then, the other day, the gable of our barn fell down for lack of proper roofing, and that must be repaired the first thing. And then I must go to the assize at such a place on account of your land in that place, which brings me in nothing or very little, and I have been put to great expense."

"Ha, sir, I knew well you would remember nothing but that land of mine."

Whereupon she turns on the other side and says:

"In God's name, let me be, for I shall never speak of it again."

"Lord love us!" says the goodman, "You wax wroth without cause."

"Not so, sir," says she. "For if you had nothing of my land, it is no fault of mine. And you know well I was asked in marriage by such and such a man and by more than twenty others who sought me only for myself; and you know that you came back and forth so often I would have none but you. Because of that I was in ill repute with my father and still am, for which I heartily reproach myself, for I think I am the unhappiest woman alive. And I pray you, sir," says she, "to tell me if the wives of such and such an one who sought to have me, are in the state I am in? And yet they are not of so noble a house as I.

By Saint John, the gowns they give their serving-wenches are better than those I wear on Sundays! I know not how many good people die, which is a pity but, please God! I shall not live long! At least you would be quit of me and would not have any more displeasure of me! "

" By my faith! " says he, " my sweet, that is ill said, for there is nothing I would not do for you, but you should look to our fortunes. Turn over to me and I will do what you will."

" *Pour Dieu*," says she, " Let me be, for by my faith, I want it not. Would to God you never wanted it more than I: for then you would never touch me."

" No ? " says he.

" Most certainly not," says she.

Then to tempt her, as he thinks, he says to her: " If I were to die you would soon be married to another."

" Fie! Fie! " says she, " for all the pleasure I have had from it! I swear by God never would lips of man touch mine, and if I knew I would outlive you, I would see to it that I went first."

And she begins to weep.

Thus the good lady comports herself (though she thinks quite the contrary), and the goodman is both glad and grieved: glad because he sees that she is cold and chaste and also because she loves him so much; grieved because he sees her weeping, for which he is sorely afflicted and will never be happy until she is comforted; he will strive in innumerable ways to do her pleasure. But she, who is determined to gain her point, which is to have the dress, will have none of it, but will get up early and at an unwonted hour and all day will be in such ill humour that he will not have one fair word from her. When comes the next night she will go to bed; and after she is in bed, the goodman will hearken if she be asleep and will look to see if her arms be well covered and will cover her if need be.

Then she will pretend to waken; and the husband says to her:

"Are you asleep, my dear?"

"No," says she.

"Are you comforted?"

"Comforted?" says she. "My woe is a little thing. Thank God," she says with a sigh, "I must be satisfied with the worldly goods God gives me."

"*Pour Dieu*," says he, "my sweet, and it please God we shall have enough; and I have thought of one thing; that is, I shall dress you so well that I wager you will be the best dressed woman at my cousin's wedding."

"*Certes*," says she, "I shall go to no feast this year."

"By my faith, my dear, you shall and you shall have what you ask."

"What I ask!" says she. "*Certes*, I ask nothing; but so help me God if I said it not for any wish to prettify myself, I who would never go out of our house save to church... But I said it for the words the other women spoke among themselves. I had it from my gossip who heard much talk of it and told me."

Then the poor man begins to think of the many things he has to do, that he has few chattels and that, mayhap, the dress will cost fifty or sixty gold pieces; and thinking this he sees no way to find the money. Nevertheless he must have it, for in his opinion his wife is a worthy and notable lady, and he thanks God in his heart for giving him such a precious jewel.

So he turns and twists from one side to the other and does not sleep all night because of the burden she has put on him. And sometimes it comes about that the lady is so shrewd that well she knows what is worrying him and laughs to herself under the sheets.

When morning comes, the husband, who has wrestled all night with his anxious thoughts, gets up and goes about his business.

And perhaps he buys the cloth and fur on credit, or he borrows money or pledges twenty or twenty-two pounds of his yearly income or even sells old jewels of gold or silver that belonged to his great-grandfather which his father had left him. He does so much that in the end he comes home provided with everything the lady required of him; but the latter, feigning lack of interest, curses all those who have made such costly display fashionable; and when she sees that he has brought the cloth and the lining she says to him:

"My dear, do not reproach me in days to come that, for my sake, you spent your money, for I would not give a sou for the most beautiful dress in the world, but only to go warmly clad."

In short, the dress is made, the girdle and the hood which, perchance, are shown off at many a church and many a dance.

But the day comes when the man must pay his creditors and the poor man cannot pay and they will not wait and will have his goods sold or himself excommunicated. And the lady hears word of it and witnesses the distraint; and perhaps they take the beautiful things for which the debt was made. Now it may come about that after the excommunication, his estate worsens and the lady must stay indoors. And God knows the pleasure and joy in which the good man lives and spends his days; for the lady rages through the houses, weeping and saying:

"Cursed be the day when I was born! Why did I not die in my cradle? Alas! Never has such great shame been done to a woman of my house; I who had been so pampered! Alas!" says she, "I work so hard to oversee my household and all I can do and save is lost. I could have married more than twenty times had I desired and where I would have had great honours and riches; for well I know how their wives fare at this hour. Poor wretched me! Why does not Death come to release me?"

Thus the lady complains and thinks not of the part she has played in it, of the gowns and jewels she must needs have, of the banquets and wedding feasts to which she went when she should have been at home thinking of her household; but she puts all the blame upon the poor man who, mayhap, has no blame at all. And he is so cast down by the law of the debt that he does not know it is all her fault.

Do not ask what painful thoughts come to the poor man who neither sleeps nor rests, but can only think how to appease his wife and pay off his debt. But what distresses him most is that the lady herself is unhappy. So he languishes and falls into penury and with great difficulty will he ever recover therefrom, for so brought down is he.

So he lives in great suffering which he takes to be joy, for he is caught in the trap he was so eager to enter and perhaps he would not be outside. There he will waste his life in worry and torment, but would not have it otherwise. Thus he will languish ever and there he will end his days miserably.

THE SECOND JOY

The second joy is when the lady feels richly dressed, as we have said, and knows well that she is comely (even if she is not, she believes she is) and goes to numerous feasts, gatherings and pilgrimages; and sometimes her husband is not pleased; and for that she arranges with her gossip and her cousin who, perhaps, is no kin at all, but she is wont to say so and for good reason. And even her mother, who sometimes, knows the business, tells the poor man that he is her cousin to lighten his heart if it is heavy. Occasionally the husband, who does not wish her to go, will say that he has no horse or some other cause. Then the gossip will say:

"*Par Dieu*, my goodman or my cousin, I do not wish to go to the feast at this time, for I have many things to do at home; but so help me God, if it were not for your honour and mine, I would not have spoken of it. And, in faith, I well know that my cousin, your wife, has no pleasure in coming, for of all women she is the one who has the greatest haste to depart when she is there." Then the husband is persuaded and asks who will take them and who will go with them.

" In faith, my goodman or my cousin, there will be your lady's mother, your wife and the wife of such an one and my cousin and yours and the other women of our street or neighbourhood. I can tell you that for discretion and honour there will be as good company as would serve the daughter of a king."

And it may be that she who speaks is to have a dress or other baubles if she plays her part well, which frequently happens.

" I well know," says he, " that the company is fine and honourable, but she has much to do at home and she is always on the highroad. So be it," says he, " let her go for this time. And mark well," says he to the lady, " that you come home before evening."

Then the lady, who sees that she has permission

to leave, pretends that she does not care to go and says:

" *Par Dieu*, my dear, I have no will to go. Pray let me stay at home."

" Verily," says the cousin or gossip, " You shall come with us."

Then the husband draws the cousin aside and says to her:

" Gossip, if I did not trust you, she should not go."

" Ha, my goodman, by God who made the world, you may well do so."

The women set out on the way and they mock the goodman, telling one another that he is jealous, but he does nothing. Thither the gallants also wend their way, and perchance some among them had pressed their suit at former feasts and mean to end their business now. God knows the lady is flattered, served and honoured, for love of her husband. God knows it well! Mark how she exerts herself to dance and sing and how little she esteems her husband when she sees herself so admired and praised. Then the gallants, who see her so well dressed and so sprightly in discourse, press forward around her, one before the other; for comeliness and a forward mien in woman encourage boldness of speech in even a faint-hearted suitor. One offers her fine words, pleasant and gracious; another presses her foot with his or squeezes her hand; another looks at her sideways with a fixed and piteous gaze; another gives her a ring, a diamond or ruby; from all of which the lady may well learn their desires if she is one with any skill to understand. Whereupon she often departs from the straight and narrow path and takes pleasure and various things and perhaps worse will come.

Now the poor man has impoverished himself for his wife's estate, which estate is the cause for her going to feasts where the gallants flock from all sides, each of them, for his part, hoping to deceive the poor man. Yet is he the cause of his own shame. And it comes to pass either that, from long frequentation, the lady or her lover grows careless, or perhaps some kinsman or special friend of the goodman drops a hint to him, and he discovers the truth or suspects it. Whereupon he falls into a jealous rage, into which no wise man should ever let himself fall; for if once he knows his wife's fault, never will he be cured by any doctor. And then he will beat her and will make his case worse, for never will she be chastened; and by beating her he will but throw fuel on the fire of mad love between her and her lover, yes, even though he were to cut off her limbs. Then it comes to pass that he loses his chattels and becomes a dotard and nothing matters to him anymore. And never will she love him, save for her pastime and to torment him. There the poor man lives in despair and torment which he mistakes for joy. Now he is firmly caught in the trap and if he were not, he would hasten to put himself in. There he will waste his life in constant languishing and will end his days in misery.

THE THIRD JOY

The third joy of marriage is when, after the young man and his young wife have taken their fill of pleasures and amorous toyings, she becomes big with child and perhaps not by her husband, which often happens. Then the poor husband is plunged into worry and torment; for he must run hither and yon to procure for his lady whatever she craves; and if the lady so much as drops a pin, he must pick it up lest she prick and hurt herself. And it will be luck if she is pleased with the meat he brings her, however much trouble he has taken to find and get it for her. And it often comes about that, because of the variety of food she enjoys and the sloth in which she lives, she loses her appetite, because she is bored with common meats. She becomes capricious and yearns for new and strange things; and she must have them, whatever they are, and the goodman must trot on foot or on horseback, night and day, to find them. In nine months his lady does nothing but groan and complain and the goodman is in torment. The poor man carries all the burden of the household; he must go to bed late and rise early and attend to the household according to his degree.

Now the time of her lying-in approaches and there must be godfathers and godmothers at the disposition of the lady. Then he must work hard to get what is needed for the gossips and the nurses and the midwives who will be there to look after the lady at the birthing, and who will drink as much wine as would fill a butt. Then is his torment doubled: then in her travail the lady vows to make more than twenty pilgrimages and the poor man also makes vows to all the saints. Then the gossips gather from all sides; then must the poor man do everything he can to make them comfortable. The lady and the gossips talk and jest and make bawdy jokes and take their ease. And let it rain or freeze or hail and the husband is out of doors, one of them will say:

"Alas! The goodman suffers much out of doors."

And another replies that it can't be helped and that he enjoys it. And if it happens that there is anything they wish, one of the goodwives will say to the lady:

"Verily, my gossip, I am astonished, as are all my neighbours, that your husband thinks so little of you and of your child. Now see how it will be when you have born him five or six! It is plain that he has no love for you; and yet you did him greater honour by wedding him than ever happened to one of his house for a long time."

"Faith," says another gossip, "if my husband did this to me I would rather he had but one eye in his head."

"Gossip," says the first, "do not let him get the upper hand; for he will do the same or worse at your other childbirths."

"Cousin," says the other, "I marvel, seeing that you are a good housewife and of noble lineage and that he is not your equal as everyone knows, that you will stand this from him; and he wrongs us all."

Then the lady replies and says:

" Verily, my dear gossips and cousins, I do not know what to do nor how I can manage, so base a man and so moody as my husband is."

" Is he base ? " says one of them. " My neighbours here know well that when I married my husband it was said that he was so full of humours that he would kill me; but, *par Dieu*, my gossip, he is well tamed, thank God, for he would rather one of his arms were broken than think or say the least thing to displease me. It is true that in the beginning he thought to adopt a certain manner of speaking and doing; but, by the holy sacrament, I was too much for him and answered pertly and took the bit between my teeth so that once or twice he beat me like a mad man, and then I did worse than before and so much that I know he told my gossip here that he would never be able to cure me even were he to kill me. Thank God, I managed so that I can say or do what I please, for I always have the last word whether it be wrong or right. But the game is to the best player and you have but to act; for, gossip, I swear there is no man so wild that his wife cannot make him easy and debonnaire if she is one with the wit to do so. By my lady Saint Catherine, gossip, he would be well tamed, that is as plain as can be."

"Be careful, my cousin," says the other, "and rail at him soundly when he comes home."

Thus the poor man is given no quarter. And the gossips keep drinking like tuns and take their leave to return the next day; and they will see how she is dominated and will bitterly upbraid the goodman therefore.

When the poor man comes home bringing meat, and perhaps at great expense for which he is sorely troubled, it may be that he arrives at one or two o'clock in the night, for he has come from afar and is either eager for news of his lady and how she is, or he does not dare to sleep away from home for fear of the expense. He comes to the house and finds all the servants, both men and maids, trained to do their lady's bidding, for otherwise they would not stay there however good and loyal they might be; and he asks how she is. And the serving-wench, who is nursing her, tells him she is very sick and has eaten nothing since he left; but she is a little better this evening — however, this is all lies. At this the poor man's grief increases, and perhaps he is dripping wet and foully dressed, which often happens, and perhaps he is all muddy because his horse has fallen in a miry road. And perhaps the poor man has not eaten all day long and he will not eat till he has news of his lady and knows how she is. The nurse and the old midwives, who are in the secret and clever at such tricks, play their parts well and pull long faces. Then the goodman cannot keep from going to her and from the door of her chamber he hears her moaning softly, and he goes up to her and kneels beside the bed and asks her:

" How are you, Madam, my love ? "

" My love," says she, " I am very sick."

" Alas! " says he, " my love, and where is your pain ? "

" My love," says she, " you know that I have been weak a long time and can eat nothing."

" Madam," says he, " why have you not commanded them to make you a good mess of capon and sugar ? "

" In God's name," says she, " they made one, but it was badly made and I cannot eat one unless you make it for me."

" Faith, my sweet, I will make one that no one shall touch but me and you shall eat it for my sake."

" I will indeed, my love," says she.

Then the goodman settles to his task and cooks and burns himself with the broth or sweats to keep it from the smoke; and he scolds his servants and says they are beasts and they can do nothing.

" Verily, sir," says the old midwife who nurses his lady and considers herself a doctor for her learning, " your gossip from such a place has done nothing todai but urge my lady to eat; but today she has not tasted a thing that God makes to grow. I do not know how she fares; I have nursed many a one and another; but my lady is the weakest woman I have ever seen."

Then the goodman goes and carries his broth to his lady, and urges her and implores so much that she takes some of it for love of him, as she says, saying that it is very tasty and that what the others made was nothing. Then he orders the women to keep a good fire in her chamber and to stay near her. The goodman goes to supper; they bring him cold meats that are not only leavings of the gossips, but the leavings of the old wives which they have handled all day while they drank God knows how much. Thus he goes to bed in great mortification.

Now the next day he gets up very early and goes to see his lady and asks her how she is, and she says that she was a little better towards day but that she did not sleep all night; though in reality she has slept soundly.

"My love," he says, "which of your gossips are to come today? We must see to it that they are well supplied and also must take thought for your churching, for you have now been in bed fifteen days. My love, we must look to it, for the expenses are great."

"Ha," cries the lady. "Cursed be the day I was born and would that I had aborted my babe! Yesterday came fifteen good women, my gossips, who did you great honour by their coming and do me great honour wherever they find me; but they had no meat fit for the serving-wenches of their houses when they lie in. Well do I know that, for I have seen them. Moreover, they made great mock of it among themselves; I saw it though they did not know I did. Alas! when they are as I am now, God knows how tenderly they are looked to and carefully cherished. Alas! I have barely lain in and can scarcely stand, and you are impatient for me to be about the house, whereby I shall catch an illness that will kill me."

"For God's sake, wife," says he, "you wrong me!"

"*Par Dieu*, sir, you would I were dead and I would so, too. And by my faith, you should not have a wife. Alas! my cousin from such a place asked me if I had a new dress for my churching, but I am far from having any. And also I do not care about it and am ready to be churched tomorrow and let things go as they may. I see clearly that we must not ask friends here. Alas! I foresee that I shall have much to suffer in time to come if I should have ten or twelve children which, please God, will never be. Please God I shall never have anymore and would to God that He had called me to Himself; at least I would not give you more displeasure; and I would be rid of the world's shame from which I have to suffer. But may God's will be done!"

"Shame upon you, my love," says the goodman, "you are overwrought and without cause."

"Without cause!" cries she. "*Par Dieu*! Without cause, eh... for, *par Dieu*, I can truly say that no poor woman of my degree has suffered what I have to suffer in my household."

"Now come, fair lady," says he, "I am glad you shall be churched when it pleases you; but tell me, pray, of what fashion would you have the dress you desire?"

"*Par Dieu*, sir, I ask none," says she, "and want none. I have dresses enough, for I care nothing for trinkets and baubles. Now that I have children, I am an old woman; and well do you

perceive it. I see clearly what will happen to me in time to come when I am worn with child-bearing and the cares of your home, as I am already. For I see my cousin, the wife of one who asked me in marriage, and he laboured hard to win me and, as long as I was free, he would not marry anyone else. And the first time I saw you, I was so mad for you that I would not have taken the son of the King of France. Now I know better how to esteem myself. But I look like the mother of his wife, though I was but a girl when she was a young lady; and it is not for any pleasure I have had, God be praised for all."

"Fie upon you," says he, "leave those words and let us take thought as to what shall be done and where I shall find the money. *Par Dieu*, my love, you know our estate well. If we spend now what little money we have, we shall be penniless, and if anything happens to us, we shall not know where to find money without harm to our goods. And you know that we have to pay for such and such a thing within eight days or we shall be in great difficulty."

" *Par Dieu*, sir," says she, " I do not ask anything of you. Alas! " says she, " much evil God wished me when he set me in such tribulation. I pray you, leave me now, for my head is splitting and you have no idea what pain I suffer. I suggest we send word to our gossips not to come, for I am feeling far from well."

" My love," says he, " they shall come and be glad of it."

" Sir, " says she, " let me be, and do as you wish."

Then comes one of the old wives who nurses the lady and says to the good man:

" Sir, do not trouble her with speech, for it is very dangerous for a woman that has a weak brain and is feeble and by no means portly." Then she draws the bed-curtain.

So the lady refuses to conclude with the goodman, because tomorrow she is expecting her gossips who play their parts well and will so soundly chastise him with arguments that straightway he will be so tamed you could lead him on the leash to guard sheep. Now for his part the husband prepares for dinner, according to his degree, and works hard at it; and will use in it more than half the food he had planned in the beginning because of his wife's attacks on him. And meanwhile the gossips arrive and he welcomes them and the goodman goes to meet them and makes them good cheer; and he does not wear a hood in the house, so amiable is he, and seems a fool though he is not. He leads the gossips towards his lady in her chamber and goes in first to her and says:

"My love, here are your gossips who have come to visit you."

"*Ave Maria*," says she, "I would rather they were in their own homes, and they would be if they knew the pleasure they give me."

"My love," says the good man, "I pray you, make them good cheer."

Then the gossips enter: they have breakfast, they dine, they eat their fill; now they drink beside their gossip's bed, now in the wine cellar, and they ruin more provisions and wine than would fill a tun; and perchance they go to the barrels where there is only one tun. And the poor man, who has all the worry and expense, goes often to see how the wine is when he sees them drinking so heavily. One of them gives him a piece of her mind, another glances at him covertly: in short, everything is consumed; the gossips wondrously befuddled depart, chattering and cackling, and pay no heed to the source. The poor man runs day and night and hunts for the dress above-mentioned and other things for which perchance he goes heavily into debt. Then is he welcome and he must listen to the baby's song; now he must go in fear of the nurse; now the lady will say that ever since she has had a child she has never been well; now he is obliged to think of paying for the expenditures he has made; now he must cut down on his estate and enlarge his wife's; now must he be content with one gown a year and two pairs of shoes, one for working days and the other for holy days, and a loose girdle every two or three years. Then he has entered into the trap he was so eager to enter and he would not be outside; and he wastes his life in suffering and in torments which he takes for joys, seeing that he would not be otherwise. So there he is and there he shall languish always and end his days miserably.

THE FOURTH JOY

The fourth joy of marriage is when he that has been happily married for six or seven, nine or ten years, more or less, and has five or six children, and has all the evil days, the evil nights and the aforesaid misfortunes behind him, or some of them, wherefore he has had many a restless night, and his youthful fires are greatly cooled so that he would rest if he could. For he is so crushed, so weary, so worn down by worries and cares that he no longer gives ear to his wife's sayings and doings, but is as hardened as an old donkey, accustomed to endure the goad, whereby he moves no faster than he is wont to move.

The poor man looks around and sees one daughter, or two, or three, ripe for marriage and eager for it as is plain to be seen, for they are merry and always ready for fun and frolic. And it may be that the goodman has no great resources and his daughters and other children are in need of gowns, shoes, slippers, doublets, victuals and many other things. Moreover he must maintain his daughters in fine estate for three reasons: first, that they may soon be asked in marriage by several gallants; another, that the daughters shall be of good courage and a cheerful countenance and never would they be otherwise; and the third is that, if the goodman refuses to so do, it shall profit him nothing, for his lady, who has passed the same way as her daughters, will not suffer it. And, perchance, if they be not maintained handsomely, they will nonetheless find ways to have their gewgaws — but about this I shall keep silent. Thus the poor man, harassed on all sides by the great burdens he has to bear, will be miserably dressed and will not care if he lives or dies, and great is his suffering for the fish in the trap would yet have some ease were he allowed to languish in it, but they shorten his days. This is what happens to the goodman who is caught in the snare of matrimony with the torments whereof I speak, and countless others.

And because of the burdens aforesaid and all he has to do, as I have said, he cares for nothing but to be allowed to live; and he is as indifferent as a tired horse that is unaware of the spurs or of anything that is done to him. Nonetheless he must trot hither and yon through the country to see to his land or his merchandise, according to his estate. Perhaps he has two miserable nags, or one, or none at all. Now he goes six or ten leagues to attend to some business. Another time he goes twenty or thirty leagues to the assize for some old, ruinous case that has come down from the days of his great-grandfather. He has a pair of boots that are two or three years old and so often have they been mended that they are a foot short and shapeless, for the part that should be at the knee does not come to the middle of the leg. And he has a pair of old style spurs from the days of King Clothaire, one of which lacks a rowel. And he has a trimmed gown that he has had five or six years, but he has not worn it save upon holy days or when they go visiting; and it is old style because, since it was made, a new fashion has come in. And whatever toy or instrument of music he sees, he is always reminded of his household and can take no pleasure in anything he sees. He lives very meanly on the road, and his horses likewise — if he has any. He has a varlet, all tatters and rags, who has an old sword his master won in the Battle of Flanders, or elsewhere, and a gown that everyone can see was not cut for him, or at least it was not cut to his measure for the seams on the shoulders come too low. He carries an old saddlebag wherein the goodman bore his armour to the Battle of Flanders; or he has other clothes according to his estate.

In short, the goodman does the best he can and at the least expense, for there are enough at home to spend. And he is ignorant of the law and is roughly handled by lawyers, sergeants and clerks of the court. And as soon as possible he departs for his house, for the affection he has for it, and also because he would not tarry on the road for the expense which is very great. It may be that he arrives home at such an hour that it is as near to morning as to evening and he finds nothing to eat, for the lady and all her household have gone to bed. And he suffers it all patiently, for well is he accustomed to it. And as for me, I believe that God sends adversity only upon those. He knows are easy and debonnaire to endure it patiently; and He sends cold only upon those that are well supplied with gowns. And if it happens that the goodman comes home early, very weary and worn, and his heart is heavy and anguished by his labours and he thinks to be well received as he has been many times, the lady will scold and rage through the house. And know that whatever the goodman orders, the servants will have none of it, for they are all obedient to the lady; and she has impressed upon them all that if they do anything contrary to her dictates, they must seek service elsewhere, and they know the lady well; and therefore he wastes his breath giving orders if it does not please the lady. If the poor varlet, who has been with him, asks anything for himself or for his horses, he is suspect and refused and dare say naught.

And thus the goodman, who is docile and has

no wish to quarrel or to annoy his family, takes all patiently and sits far from the fire, though he is very cold; but the lady and her children are close beside it; and perhaps he sees the lady's expression that is ill-tempered and sour, and she pays no heed to him, nor does she offer him supper, but scolds constantly with harsh words that wound the poor man who says not a word. And it often happens that, because of his hunger and travail and for his wife's doings which he sees so marvelous, for she pretends there is nothing in the house to eat, the goodman tries to be angry and says:

"Verily, lady, you do yourself well! I am weary and worn and have neither eaten nor drunk this day, and I am wet to my shirt and you pay me no heed and offer me naught to eat nor otherwise."

"By my faith, you have done a marvelous thing! Because you took the varlet away there was none here to put my flax to dry for me, and I have lost more by my linen than you could earn in four years! I have long told you to lock your chicken-pen where the weasel ate three of my brooding hens, wherefore you will see much damage. And, *par Dieu*, if you live, you will be the poorest fellow of our house."

"Fair lady," says he, "Do not speak such words. God be thanked, I have enough and, if it please God, I shall have, and I come of honest lineage."

"Fie upon you!" says she, "Your family! Holy Mary, I know not where they are, for I see none that are worth aught."

"My God, lady," says he, "there are good men among them."

"And what good are they to you?" says she.

"What good are they to me?" says the goodman. "But what good are yours to me?"

"What good are my kin to you?" says the lady. "I swear to God you were but a mean fellow were it not for them."

"By my troth," says he. "Now enough of such talk!"

"*Certes*," says she. "They would answer you well were you to speak of it to them."

Then the goodman is silent, for perhaps he

fears lest she tell her kin that he spoke ill of them, since she comes of better lineage than he.

And then one of the children begins to cry and perhaps it is the one the goodman loves best. And the lady takes a switch and beats the child hard, more to spite the goodman than anything else. Then the goodman says to her:

" Fair lady, do not beat him ! " And he would seem to be full of wrath. And the lady says:

" Devil take it! You have not the trouble of bringing them up and they cost you nothing But I am about them day and night! May the plague take them! "

" Ha! Fair lady," says he, " that is ill said."

" Look you, sir," says the nurse, " you know not the trouble my lady has and that they give us in rearing them."

" By my faith," says the serving-wench, " you should be ashamed when you come home and the house should be rejoiced at your coming, and you do naught but rage."

" What rage mean you ? " says he. " Faith, I do not rage."

Then all the household is against him and so the goodman, seeing himself attacked from all sides, as he has been many a time, and knowing well that he has nothing to gain, goes to bed *sans* supper, *sans* fire, soaked to the skin, and chilled to the bone. And should he sup, God only knows how and in what ease and comfort. So he goes to bed and hears the children cry in the night; and perhaps the lady and the nurse let them cry on purpose to spite the goodman. Thus the night passes in griefs and torments which he takes for great joys, seeing he would not be otherwise. For he is in the trap and there he will be always and will end his days miserably.

THE FIFTH JOY

The fifth joy is when the poor man, who is married, is weary and worn from the great labour and woes he has endured and the fires of his youth are banked; and perhaps his wife is of a nobler house than he or younger, both of which are two serious matters. For there is nothing more destructive to a man then to become entangled in those two bonds that are so contrary to nature and to reason.

Sometimes they have children and sometimes they do not. Nonetheless, the lady has not such travail as the goodman, who has laboured to keep her at her ease and in the estate which she has ever had fair and with great possessions. And as if that were not enough, he must do even more; for she would not debase her lineage and her husband must think himself greatly honoured that God has granted him the grace to wed her. And it frequently happens that when they quarrel, she tells him as a threat that her kin gave her not to him for his lechery and that well she knows what belongs to her birth. And she says that if she were to write to her brothers or to her cousins they would come at once to fetch her. And for this he dare not raise a hand to her, whatever his lips may say. Thus, it seems to me, he is in great bondage. And it may well be that her parents would have married her more nobly and would not have given her to the goodman had it not been for a little escapade she had in her youth, I know not from what mishap that comes from being passionate and in love, of which the goodman knew nothing. Or mayhap he has heard talk of something, but the goodman who is honest and trusting hears many good folk swear that it was naught but evil slanders, ugly lies and unfounded, against the good lady or citizenness; for some women are falsely accused, God knows it well, by the young gallants that go roistering about the streets and talk boldly of good and virtuous women when they can get no more from them.

Thus the good woman sees that her husband has given up all frolicking and all joys and thinks only of acquiring wealth and lands. And perhaps he has not great resources, wherefore he is niggardly at spending money, which does not please the lady, for she would often have new things such as gowns, girdles and other things that she sees in the good company she often frequents at dances and feasts with her cousins and gossips and with her male cousin who, perhaps, is no kin at all.

And sometimes it comes to pass that, because of the great ease in which she lives and because of the great delights and pleasure she takes in divers feasts and dances to which she goes continually and where she sees and hears certain matters spoken of, she scorns her husband and takes a lover as it pleases her. And thus never will she love her husband for he is quite other than her lover; he is miserly, distraught with thoughts and cares, and she has not yet come to his state of miserliness and is in the full bloom of her youth which she would spend in dallyings and delights.

Therefore she often goes where she may see her gay and lively young lover. And sometimes it happens that she has long failed to see him at her will, but she sends a message that she must see him on the morrow at a certain hour.

And when evening comes and the goodman, her husband, goes to bed and would frolic with her, she remembers her lover whom she is to see on the morrow at a certain hour, and finds a way to put him off and will not consent and says she is sick. For she thinks naught of him, a poor thing in comparison with her lover whom she has not seen for eight days or more and who will come on the morrow more ravenous and tempestuous than ever. For perhaps he has languished long in street and garden and they have not been able to speak to each other, wherefore when he comes on the morrow, he will do marvels, as much from appetite as from haste. Perhaps, also, they will have much leisure, making one to the other all the pleasures man can desire. And know that she does a hundred things with her lover and shows him amorous secrets and caresses she dare not show her husband. And likewise her lover will give her all the pleasure he may and many little caresses to her delight such as no husband might ever do. For even if the husband knew them before he was married, he has forgotten them, for he has grown careless and dulled to such things. Moreover he would not do them, for he would think he was teaching his wife things of which she was innocent. While the lady has a lover at will and they can meet and there is time, they make each other such cheer as no man may describe, so that hereafter she has no esteem for her husband. And after those pleasures the lady takes as much delight in frolicking with her husband as a wine-taster does in a musty wine after a rare hypocras or a good Burgundy. For sometimes when he who has a great thirst, drinks a poor or musty wine, he finds it good enough as he drinks it because of the great thirst he has; but when he has drunk, he notices a bad after-taste and would never drink of it again save for lack of a better. Know also that the lady who has her lover at pleasure, from necessity and lack of a better, sometimes accepts her husband's request to quench her thirst and pass the time. But when her husband would take thereof and she would not, she says to him:

"Forsooth," says she, "let me be and wait till morning."

"*Certes*, my love," he will say, "I shall not wait. Turn towards me."

"*Par Dieu*, my dear," she will say, "you will please me much if you would let me bide till morning."

Then the lady turns away and the goodman, who dare not displease her, leaves her alone till morning. But the lady, thinking of her lover and meaning to see him the next day, which is not the same thing, says to herself that her husband shall not touch her in the morning. Wherefore she rises betimes and bustles about pretending to be a good housekeeper and leaves him asleep. And perhaps she sees her lover and takes her pleasure before the goodman is up; and afterwards she is too busy about the house. Sometimes it happens that she does not rise, but before dawn she begins to complain and groan deliberately. And the goodman hears her and asks:

"Where is your pain, my love?"

"Verily, my dear, I have such a great pain in my side and in my belly as you never knew. Methinks it is the sickness I am wont to suffer."

"My love," says he, "turn towards me."

"*Par Dieu*, my dear," says she, "I am marvelous hot and cannot sleep."

Then the goodman embraces her and finds that she is very hot and he says: "Truly!" But the malady is other than he imagines, for perhaps she has dreamed she was with her lover and is sweating profusely. Then the husband covers her carefully lest the air should blow upon her to make her dry her sweat, and he says:

"My love, take care you do not catch cold and I will order the household." Then the husband rises, perhaps *sans* fire and *sans* candle; and when it is time for her to get up, he has a fire built for her; and the lady sleeps at her ease and laughs to herself.

Another time the goodman wishes to frolic with

her and she, who has excused herself divers times, as aforesaid, will find means to beguile him, if she may, for she thinks naught of his prowess. Nevertheless the goodman has need thereof and kisses and caresses her and God knows what pleasure she has if she is such as we have said. She speaks thus:

" Please God, my dear, you would never do it save when I spoke of it first."

" What," says he, " would you never do it ? "

" By my soul, my dear, no! Not I! And methinks I deserve better. And had I known as much before I was wed, I would never have been a wife."

" Forsooth! " says he, " Then why did you marry ? "

" By my faith, my dear, I know not. I was but a child and did what my father and mother told me " (though perhaps she had sampled it well beforehand).

" What do you mean ? " says he. " I always find you of this same mind; I know not why it may be."

"By my soul, my love, if it were not your pleasure, I would never want it."

When he hears this the goodman is very pleased and he says to himself that she is a cold woman and that she cares nothing for it; and perhaps she is fair of skin and feminine and slight of figure, whereby he is all the more sure of it. Then he kisses her and embraces her and has his way with her; and the lady, thinking of another, wishes she were elsewhere and lets him have his way and lies there as unwieldy as a stone and does not help him. And the goodman is heavy and clumsy and is not so skilled as others. The lady turns her face to one side; for this is not the good wine she has had at other times, wherefore she is bored. "My dear," she says to him, "you are crushing me and moreover, my dear, you will do yourself harm."

The goodman is afraid to continue lest he displease his lady. Thus she leads him such a dance that he thinks she is not strong because perhaps she is pale, wherefore he believes it the more readily.

It may be, perhaps, that the lady would have a new gown or something else from her husband, and well she knows his estate and that he is niggardly about spending his money. So she waits for a good moment to get what she asks. And when they are in their bedchamber in the midst of their delights and pleasures, she shows him such good cheer that it is a marvel. For a clever woman knows a thousand new devices to make good cheer when she will. And the goodman, who is not used to such good cheer, is well pleased. Then she caresses him and kisses him, and the goodman says:

" Verily, my sweet, I think you would ask somewhat of me."

" *Par Dieu*, my dear, I ask naught of you save to make good cheer. Please God," says she, " that I never know another paradise save to be always in your arms! Forsooth, I would have none other. Verily," says she, " so help me God, my lips have never touched man's save yours and your cousins and mine, when they come here and you bid me kiss them. But I think there is no man on earth so gentle and so gracious as you."

"No, my love?" says he. "There was such a cavalier who hoped to wed you."

"Fie, fie," says she, "upon my soul, when first I saw you, though from afar and I had but a glimpse of you, never would I have taken another even had he been the king's son, the dauphin of France. Methinks that God so willed it; for my father and my mother would have married me to him but never would I do it. I know not why it is, methinks it was fate."

Then they take their pleasure and the lady shows herself agile and eager. Then she says to the goodman:

"My love," says she, "do you know what I would ask of you? I pray you refuse me not."

"By my word, my love, I shall grant it if I may."

"My love," says she, "You know the wife of such a one now has a gown lined with good grey or miniver. I pray you that I may have one. By my soul, I say it not from any desire to be gaily apparelled, but because methinks you are indeed in such estate to clothe me honourably, and more so than her husband. As for me, her person is not to be compared to mine. I say it not in praise of myself but, *par Dieu*, because she is so proud rather than for any other reason."

Then the goodman who, perhaps, is miserly, or who thinks she has gowns enough, gives some thought to it and then says to her:

"My love, have you not gowns enough?"

"*Par Dieu*, my dear," says she, "Yes, and as for me, I care not if I were dressed in coarse stuff. But we are shamed by her."

"Pay no heed, my love. Let them talk. We shall not borrow from them."

"*Par Dieu*, my love, truly! But I am gowned like a serving-wench compared to her. I count for nothing beside my sister, though I am older than she, which is a sorry thing."

Perhaps the goodman will grant her what she asks, which is a pity for him, for she will but be more eager to go to feasts and dances than before. And the fur will help in a way he has never dreamed of.

And if he does not give her the gown, know that, since she is light of heart and debonnaire, she has made up her mind to have it no matter whence it comes and whatsoever it may cost. And perhaps she has a lover, but he is not rich enough to give it to her, for mayhap he is but a poor gallant whom she supports according to his degree.

Wherefore she will cast her eye upon some other gallant who, but the other day, desired to give her a diamond at a feast and afterwards sent her twenty or thirty golden écus or more by her serving-wench. But she did not wish to accept them so quickly. And as she had refused them harshly, she will now give him another gracious glance, whereupon the charming gallant will speak again to the lady's serving-wench whom he will meet on the way to the fountain or elsewhere. And he will say:

"Jehanne, my good wench, I have something to say to you."

"Sir," says she, "as you please."

"Wench," says he, "you know the love I bear

your mistress. I pray you tell me does she ever speak of me."

"Faith," says the serving-wench, "she says naught but all good, and I know she wishes you no harm."

"*Par Dieu*, Jehanne, my pretty, "says he, "Do not forget me and commend me to her and, by my faith, you shall have a new gown and you will see that I shall give it to you."

"*Certes*," says she, "I will not take it."

"*Par Dieu*," says he. "Yes, you shall. And I pray you let me have news from you on the morrow."

The serving-wench goes home and says to her lady:

"By my faith, Madam, I have found one who is in a fine fettle."

"And who is that?" says the lady.

"By my soul, my lady, it is such a one."

"And what did he say to you?" says she.

"By my faith, he is pale with love and in such a state he knows not what he does."

"*Par Dieu*, Jehanne, " says she. "Is he a fair and comely man?"

" Verily," says she, " You say truly, the comeliest I have ever seen. He is rich and cut out to be a devoted lover and would do much good to his lady."

" *Par Dieu*, Jehanne," says the lady. " I can get naught from my husband; he does all things badly."

" By all the saints, my lady, but it is great folly to suffer so much."

" *Par Dieu*, Jehanne, I am so fond of the one you know and for so long that my heart would never be given to another."

" Forsooth, my lady, it is folly to put one's heart on any man in this world, for they have no consideration for poor women, once they are lords over them, such traitors are they. And you know, my lady, that he can do you no good, but he costs you enough to keep him according to his degree. And for God's sake, my lady, he of whom I spoke, told me he would keep you in great estate; and you are not to trouble yourself about gowns, for you will have enough and of all sorts, but trouble only to find a way to speak to my lord who has given them to you."

"Verily, Jehanne, I know not what to do."

"By my soul, my lady, make up your mind, for I have promised him to speak with him on the morrow."

"What shall we do, Jehanne?"

"My lady, leave it to me. Tomorrow I shall go to the fountain and I know he will be on the way to speak to me. But I shall tell him that you will not grant his request, for all I might say to you, so great is your fear of dishonour. From that he will take hope; and thereafter, we shall speak more of the matter and methinks I shall arrange it well."

Then the serving-wench goes to the fountain in in the morning and meets the gallant who has waited some three hours and she makes him wait on purpose, for if he did not have to pay dearly for his love, he would not value it. He comes up to her and greets her and she him.

"What news, Jehanne, my pretty?" says he. "How is your mistress?"

" Faith," says she, " she sits at home, all pensive and melancholy."

" And wherefore ? " says he.

" Faith, my master is so harsh that she has a very bad time."

" Aha! " says he. " Cursed be the villainous gaoler."

" Amen," says she, " for we cannot abide him in our house."

" Now tell me, Jehanne, what said she to you ? "

" Faith," says she, " I spoke to her of it, but she will never consent; for she has such great fear of her lord that it is a marvel; and she has to do with a hard man. And even if she did desire it, she could not, so closely is she guarded by her father and her mother and all her brothers. I think the poor lady has not spoken with a man since I have lived with her — and that is four, years — save to you the other day. Nonetheless she cannot forget you and well do I know (as far as I can tell) that were she to love any, she would not refuse you for another."

" Jehanne," says he, " I beg you to do this

for me and, by my faith, you shall command me forever."

"Upon my word," says she, "I spoke to her of it for your sake; for, by my faith, never do I meddle in such matters."

"Alas, good wench," says he, "advise me what to do."

"Upon my word," says she, "the best will be that you speak to her. And this is the right moment, for her husband has refused to give her a gown she asked of him and she is very angry. I advise you, be at church tomorrow and salute her and tell her boldly your problem and offer her what you wish to give her, though well do I know she will take naught. But she will admire you all the more and will know your largesse and your valor."

"Alas, Jehanne, would that she might take what I offer her."

"Faith," says she, "she will never take it. For you never saw a more honest woman nor a sweeter one. Let me have what you would give her and I will try to make her take it. At least I will do my best."

"Verily, Jehanne, you say well."

Jehanne comes to her lady, laughing.

"What are you laughing at, Jehanne?" says the lady.

"By my soul, there are some who are not very merry."

"How is that?" says she.

"*Certes*, Madam, he will speak to you on the morrow at church."

Then she tells her what to do. "Be modest," she says, "and hold him off, but at the same time do not rebuff him too harshly, but keep him betwixt hope and fear."

Then the lady goes to church and the gallant has been there three hours, in great devotion, God knows. He stands where it would be bad manners not to give holy water to the lady and the other women of estate who are with her, and they thank him, but the poor man would do them a much greater service if he could and if it were their pleasure. He notes that the lady is alone on her bench with her profile towards him, telling her rosary. She is prettily decked out and looks as demure as a saint. He goes up to her and they whisper together; but she will grant him naught and will take naught from him; but always replies in such a way that well he knows she loves him and only fears dishonour, wherefore he is very happy.

They part. The lady and the serving-wench take counsel together and make their plan. And the serving-wench says:

"Well do I know, my lady, that he is eager to speak with me now, but I shall tell him you will do naught, whereby I am sore distressed, so great is my pity for him. And I shall tell him my master has gone away and that he shall come after nightfall and I shall let him into the house and lead him to your chamber, as if you knew naught thereof. Thus you will feign to be greatly vexed thereat. And make him labour sore that he may prize you all the more. And say you will cry aloud and will summon me. And as you have taken naught, he will prize you the higher and will give you more lavishly than if you had taken somewhat first. But I will have with me what he is to give you, for he must bring it to me on the morrow; and then I will tell him you would take naught thereof. And then I shall tell him, when the thing is done, that he shall give them to you to buy a gown. And in his presence you shall scold me harshly for having taken it and not having given it back. Nonetheless, I will put the money in safekeeping; for, *par Dieu*, my lady, some men are so wondrously clever they have deceived many a lass."

" So be it, Jehanne. Do as you wish."

Then Jehanne goes off and finds the gallant who asks for news of his lady.

" *Par Dieu*," says she, " I had to begin all over again with her. But because I have meddled in this, I would have you both agreed, for I fear she will betray me to her husband or her kin. But I know could I make her take what you offer her, all would be well. And by the saints, I will try to make her take it; and this is the moment, for her husband has refused her a gown she covets marvellously."

Then the gallant gives her twenty or thirty golden écus and Jehanne says to him:

"This is my advice. *Par Dieu*, sir, you are an honourable gentleman and I know not what is the matter with me, for on my word, I have never done for any man what I am doing for you. And well do you know the great danger I run, for if my master knew but one word of it, I would be lost. But because of the affection I have for you, I shall do a thing for which I shall put myself in danger. Well do I know she loves you dearly: and because my master is not at home, come in very quietly by our back gate at twelve o'clock tonight and I will lead you to her chamber. She sleeps soundly for she is but a child; and you shall lie with her, for no other way do I see, and mayhap your desire will be granted. For it is a great thing when two are naked and in the dark; for she who would repulse you by day, would not do so by night in such a case."

"Aha! Jehanne, my pretty," says the gallant, "I thank you. You shall always share my last penny."

When night comes the gallant arrives as Jehanne has arranged, and of course she has told all to her lady. He gets into bed very quietly; and when she, who is feigning sleep, feels herself embraced, she trembles and says:

" Who is that? "

" My dear love," says he, " it is I. "

" By all the saints, this will not do! " She feigns to rise and call Jehanne. But Jehanne does not answer and is not there when needed, which is a great pity. And when she realizes that Jehanne does not answer:

" Ha! I am betrayed! "

Then they wrestle together in many a way and in the end the poor lady can do no more and, panting, is forced to yield — which is a great pity for she is only a poor lone woman. And were it not for fear of dishonour she would have cried louder, but it is better to keep her good name since this is the way it must be. And so they lose themselves in the delights of lovemaking.

Thus are the affairs of the goodman, her husband, settled. And now the lady has the gown her husband refused to give her, that has cost him, and will cost him, exceeding dear. Now she arranges for her mother to give her the cloth in her husband's presence to allay any suspicions he may have; for the lady has also persuaded her mother that she bought it from the sale of a number of little baubles she sold without her husband's knowledge — and perhaps her mother knows the whole matter well, as often happens. After this gown she will need another, two or three silver girdles and other things. Whereby the husband, who is serious, cunning and sly, as I have said, becomes suspicious, and he has seen something he does not like, or perhaps a friend has told him; for in the long run all must come out. Now he gives himself over to jealous rage. Now he spies on her; now he feigns to go away and comes home suddenly at night to catch her lover, but it is not so easy to do this. Then he sulks in the house and perhaps he sees many things whereat he fumes and storms; and she replies with dignity for she feels she is of noble lineage and often reminds him of her kin who sometimes speak of it to him. Then they quarrel and never will the goodman have any joy; he will be served with lies and shall feed thereon. His resources will dwindle, his body dry up. He stays at home to see that the wind does not blow the roof off and neglects his business; in short, never will life be good for him. Thus shall he stay in the trap in which he put himself, in great torments which he thought, and still thinks, are joys. For were he not in it, he would never stop till he was inside; and he would not be otherwise. Thus will he live languishing always and end his days miserably.

THE SIXTH JOY

The sixth joy is when he who is married has suffered all the pains and travails aforesaid, or some of them, and particularly if he is young and has a wife of fickle and flighty disposition and he is a good man and has great love for her and gives her all the pleasure he can; and though she is a notable woman, she intends to keep the upper hand and to know her husband's business and she is given to interfering and answering back if need be. And such is the nature of that woman that whatever husband she had, and though she were happy and lacked for nothing, yet would she always give her husband something to think about or suspect.

And sometimes when the husband and his wife are in their bedchamber all night and half a day, towards morning they are blissful and joyous and the husband leaves her in the bedchamber, where she prettifies herself and clothes herself gaily, smiling happily, and he goes off to order dinner and attend to the household chores. And when it is time to dine, he calls the lady. But one of the servants or one of the children comes and tells him the lady will not dine.

"Go and bid her come," says he.

Then the servant or the child goes and says to her:

"Madam, my lord bids you to come and dine, for he will not eat till you are there."

"Go and tell him," says she, "that I will not dine."

"Go tell her to come," says he.

Then she makes her reply and the goodman goes to ask what the trouble is and is greatly astounded, though he has seen her act thus before. But for all his asking, he shall have nothing; and verily, there is nothing that ails her, but she feigns there is. And perhaps she will not come to dinner, no matter what he may do. Sometimes he does so much that she comes and, with her hand on his arm, like a bride, they go to dinner; and the meat is cold, so long has it been kept waiting. And again she argues and makes such a fuss that she will not eat, nor he either, for he is fool enough to be troubled thereat. And the more he would have her in good cheer, the more melancholy she becomes to worry him. For to win the man who loves her and does his best to please her, a woman has only to make him worry about her; whereas to win the favour of a man who cares naught for her, she must show him good cheer and loving services. And she thinks she does well to burden her husband with many cares and tribulations.

Sometimes the goodman may go away on business and bring home one or two of his friends with him, because he has business with them or they with him. But sometimes it happens that, when he is absent, as we have said, he sends a varlet to his wife and prays her to put the house in order to welcome the friends he is bringing with him, for he likes them well and does business with them. Moreover he begs her to have food prepared that they may be well received.

The varlet comes to the lady and bows and says:

"My lady," says he, "my master is on his way home and four men of estate are coming with him; and he prays that you have all well prepared that they may be well received."

"By my faith," says she, "I shall have naught to do with it; I have naught to do with his feasts. Why has he not come himself?"

"I know not, my lady, but thus he spoke to me."

"God help me," says she, "You are a bad servant and you meddle too much."

Then the varlet is silent, and the lady goes into her chamber and will do nothing and, what is worse, she will send all her servants from home, some here and some there; and her daughters, if she has any, or her serving-wenches, know well what to say to the goodman when he comes home. So then the goodman arrives and calls. And one of his daughters or one of the serving-wenches answers him. Then the goodman asks if all is prepared.

"Faith, sir," says she, "Madam is very ill. Naught has been done."

The goodman is distressed and leads his friends into the great hall or elsewhere according to his estate, where there is no fire and nothing prepared. Do not ask if he is pleased. For perhaps the friends he has brought have noticed that he sent the varlet ahead, whereby they note well that nothing the goodman orders is done.

The goodman storms and summons his servants; but perhaps he finds only one wretched varlet, or a poor old woman who can do naught, whom perhaps the lady has kept at home because she knows they can do naught. He comes into his wife's chamber and says to her:

"Fair lady, why have you not done what I bade you do?"

"Sir," says she, "You bid so many things of one sort and the other that we do not know what to believe."

"By the saints!" says he, scratching his head, "You have given me the greatest displeasure, for in all the world I am bound to no men more than these."

"And what is that to me, sir," says she. "What would you have me do? What right have you to be feasting guests? By my faith, it seems you lack good sense. But, after all, do as you please, I care not!"

"I ask you, fair lady, why you sent the servants from home?"

"And how did I know," says she, "that you would need them?" When really she had sent them all away to spite the goodman.

Then he, who would amend the ill done, ceases to speak and goes off, woefully, for perhaps he would rather have lost one hundred gold écus than to have such men insulted. But the lady cares not a wit. She knows him well: he will not bite, for she has seen him of old. In short, he runs about the house and rallies those of his servants he can find and does the best he can. Then the goodman asks for a tablecloth and some white, bordered napkins; but they bring him some he cannot use. He goes to the lady and tells her that those gentlemen, who are his kin and his particular friends, have asked repeatedly for her; and he begs her sweetly to come and see them and give them good cheer.

"And what shall I do?" says she.

"My love, I beg of you to come, for my sake."

"*Certes*," says she, "I shall not go; they are too fine gentlemen and they have no regard for poor women." Then perhaps she goes. And if she goes, she will look so sour and be so ungracious that it would have been better for the goodman had she not come at all. For, from her manner, his friends well know their presence is not to her liking. And if she does not go and the goodman asks her for towels and napkins:

"Towels?" says she, "there are prettier ones already laid out than they have ever used and for nobler gentlemen than they. And when my brother or my cousin, who are of as high degree as they are, come here they never have any others. And, moreover, all the others are in the wash. I do not say that, however, because of the towels, but this morning I lost my keys. Here is the serving-wench looking for them now in that bed-straw, and I know not what I have done with them, for I have so much to do that I know not which way to turn and my head is awhirl."

"Verily," says he, "I am sore dismayed. Verily, I shall break open the coffers."

"Faith," says she, "You would do well and I am waiting for you to break them."

Then he does not know what to do, and it comes to pass that he finds the key and thinks she is telling the truth, and they go to the table. Then he must have new wine, for the household wine is not good; but the bit and trace cannot be found because the lady will not have it. And there is no cheese or any other thing and perhaps they have to borrow from the neighbors. The goodman's page is with the pages of his friends in the stable and tells them how the lady feigns illness, so wroth is she that their masters are here. Now comes the time to go to bed and the goodman cannot have clean linen because the keys are lost, nor pillows, nor fine night-caps; the guests must needs sleep in common sheets. Then in the morning the friends depart, for they have seen the lady's face and their varlets tell them, on the way, what they learned from the goodman's servant. Thus they laugh and jest and make mock of him as they ride along. Nonetheless they are not pleased and they say it will be long ere they return, and it would have been better for the goodman to lose his chattels than to bring them home.

When morning comes, he goes to his lady and says:

"Verily, lady, I am sore amazed at your doings, nor would I know how to deal with you."

"*Ave Maria,*" says she, "and is there so much wrong with me? Alack! Day and night I must feed pigs, chickens, geese — and there is no end to it; and spin and toil and do the best I may, so that I shall die before my time. Nor can I have one hour's rest and you labour only to spend and waste all with men of no account to me."

"What do you mean?" the husband will say. "They are men who can help me or harm me greatly."

Then the goodman remembers that when a knight of the county, who is a great gallant, comes to the house, naught is spared; and this though the goodman has told her he would not have her bid him to the house for he has no business there. And she replies that he was the one who brought the knight there, and she has an answer for all. Then they begin to quarrel, and perhaps he will beat her; but that will be foolish. Then the goodman says to her:

"By the salvation I hope for, if ever I find him here or ever you speak to him, I shall give you the greatest beating you ever had."

"By my faith," says she, "I should not care if he were hanged; but so it is, for it is ever the guiltless that suffer. Were I a light woman, I should not be surprised, and yet I would stand better with you than I do."

Then they quarrel. And perhaps, out of malice on his part or on hers, they do not lie together for a time. And that is to her liking, for perhaps the knight of whom he spoke will come at night through the back door or a window. Later, things may be smoothed over, but the goodman is the one who must make peace and flatter her, for woman ever likes flattery; and strange as it may be, there is no lie so great that she will not believe it, be it only in her praise.

Thus time passes till perchance the goodman finds the lady talking to the above-mentioned knight at home or at a feast, whereupon he becomes even more jealous than before. He mistrusts her and is marvelously perturbed and spies and makes enquiries, which is foolish of him, for a man of noble mind should never question a woman's doings. And if the husband once knows his wife's fault, he will fall into such decline that no physician will ever cure him. Wherefore since he hunts and spies out his shame and finds it, it is but reason he should suffer the evil he seeks and hunts; and in that case I hold him to be lost. For he will ever fly into a rage with her and she will but act the worse. And he will be in danger of his life and chattels, and old age will overtake him. He will become a dotard and completely stupid. Thus is he closed in the trap with suffering and grief, which he takes for joy, seeing he would not be otherwise. And if he repents of it, it is too late. Thus will he live forever in torment and will end his days miserably.

THE SEVENTH JOY

The seventh joy of marriage is when sometimes he, who has married, finds an excellent wife, chaste and of high lineage. Moreover it sometimes happens that he finds a wife who is frolicsome and pleasure-loving and would never refuse any advances. But know that, whatever her degree, be she serious or otherwise, every woman believes in and holds to a general rule in marriage: namely, that her husband is the sorriest and least puissant in privy matters of any man in the world. And it often happens that the young man, who lives like a cock, marries a good and modest young girl and they take their pleasures together as often and as much as they can for one year, two years or more, until their youthful passion is spent. However the woman does not wear out so quickly as the man, whatever his estate, for she has not the anxieties, the travails, the cares he has;

and were he to do nothing but take his ease and delight, he would wear out sooner than she.

To be sure, so long as the wife is bearing children and is big with child, she is greatly hindered and suffers great pain at her lying-in, but that is naught compared to the responsibility a sensible man assumes or his deep thoughts concerning some great project in view. And as for the pains of of pregnancy or of lying-in, I marvel no more at it than at a hen or a goose that lays an egg as big as a fist through an opening where before a little finger could not have passed. Wherefore it is as great a feat of Nature to do the one thing as the other. Thus you will see that, by laying every day, a hen will keep fatter than a cock; for the cock is so stupid that he does nothing all day long save search for food to put in her beak, and the hen has no care but to eat and cackle and take her ease. The same do good husbands who are much praised therefor. Afterwards it may happen that the goodman, who always has worries and cares and his thoughts elsewhere, is all thin and worn; nor does he give much time to frolicking, or at least

but seldom, and then only to please his wife; and perchance he is not as lively as before, wherefore he leaves off altogether. Thus the wife is neglected, but she is just as lively as ever. And as his attentions grow less daily, the pleasures and delights they had enjoyed together when the husband was young and strong turn to strife and quarrels. And as little by little those attentions lessen, they begin to fight.

And when the lady is not satisfied with her goodman's attentions and she is a good woman and would do no wrong, she thinks that her husband is not so puissant as others; and with the best reason, for she has never known any but him and he is not enough for her. And rightly one man should suffice for a woman or Nature would not have regulated things so well and, moreover, I believe that if one man were not sufficient for one woman, God and the Church would have ordained that each woman should have two or as many as would suffice her. And sometimes some women set out to discover whether other men are as lacking as their husbands. And she who does so mayhap will think it better than before, for perhaps she takes a lover whom she can know only in great secrecy and trepidation, and he is eager and does marvels when he comes to her. And if she had thought her husband poor and feeble before, she thinks so even more now, for present pleasures are always sweeter than past memories, and this she believes more firmly than before, for experience is the teacher.

And it also happens that he who has married finds a wife who likes to make merry and will not refuse any pleas; and this woman thinks as poorly of her husband as the other woman, as I said; for perchance she has tried other men whose attentions are greater than the goodman's, for he makes no great effort knowing well he will ever find her near him.

And know that men do the contrary to what is said here: for whatsoever women they have, they generally think them better than all other women. Now and then the rule fails, but that is in the case of desperate and beastly knaves who lack understanding. Thus one gladly sees many husbands praise their wives, recounting their good virtues; and in their opinion there are none to equal them nor any where they could find such virtues, such delights or such good appetite. Thus, when a woman is a widow, one often sees that she soon remarries and sometimes she does not even wait a month to discover whether the other will be as weak and feeble as he who has died; wherefore she is neither faithful nor loyal to him.

Thus it often happens that the woman who so conducts herself ruins all by her poor management and foolishly wastes the possessions her poor husband acquired through great labour, according to his estate, and spends them in divers ways, now on her lover, now on an old bawd, now on her confessor who is a Franciscan or a Dominican friar and who receives a goodly present from her to absolve her every year, for such people like to exercise the power of the Pope. And the goodman, her husband, manages as wisely as he can and does not make great expenses and reckons what income he may have, or pension or merchandise, according to his degree and his charges.

Thus he finds, when all is reckoned over and over, that his business is not going well and he is in great woe. Then when he goes to bed, he speaks of it to his wife whom he loves better than himself, and says:

"Verily, my love, I know not why it is, but I know not what is happening to our goods, money, wheat, wine or other things. And for my part, I am always so careful in my management of our affairs that I dare not have a new gown."

"Verily, my love, I am astounded at the way you manage. I know not either what it can be, for I try to run things and manage as best I can and as smoothly."

Thus the goodman does not know where he stands and he falls into penury and does not know what to think, save that he concludes he is very unfortunate and luck has turned against him. Nor will he ever believe anything against his wife, and so he will never find anyone to speak of her to him, save by chance; for the man who would speak thereof would afterwards be the greatest enemy he could have.

And sometimes it may happen that he has a good friend who sees what lack of management there is, and cannot refrain from telling him to look to his house, without telling him more; or perhaps he will tell him the whole situation as it is, at which the goodman will be greatly astounded. Thus he will be in a bad humour, whereby his wife well knows there is something wrong and perhaps suspects the man who told him, because he had found great fault with her at one time. But, may it please God, she will get to the bottom of it. The goodman says nothing to her and thinks he will test her and says:

" My sweet, I must go on a journey, twelve leagues from here."

" What for, my love ? " says she.

" I must go there for such and such a reason," says he.

" I would rather you sent a varlet, my love," says she.

" I think that would be a mistake," says he, " but I shall return in two or three days."

Then he leaves and feigns to go on a journey

and goes into a woods and takes up his station where he will see any thing or anyone who goes into his house. And the lady, who has heard what was said to him, sends word to her lover not to come for aught in the world, for she is very suspicious.

Thus the lady manages so wisely that, God be praised, her husband will never find her out. And after the goodman has spied and listened, he feigns to return from his journey and he is in excellent humour for he believes that it is all a lie. And thus he does not believe that his wife, who welcomes him so warmly and kisses and caresses him so tenderly and calls him " my love," could ever do such a thing; moreover he sees that there is nothing to it. When he is with her, he says to his wife:

" Verily, my love, people have told me certain words that displease me."

" *Par Dieu*, my love, I know not what it is, but for some time now you have been in an ill humour. I greatly feared you might have some loss or that our friends were dead or captured by the English."

" It is not that," says he, " but it is worse than you say."

" *Ave Maria*," says she, " and what can it be ? I pray you tell me."

" *Certes*, one of my friends told me that such an one lay with you... and a number of other things."

Then the lady crosses herself, shows great surprise, smiles and says:

" My love, be not angry. By my troth, my dear, I would I were as well quit of all my sins as this one."

Then she lays her hand on his head and speaks thus:

" My love, I shall swear not only to that, but I would send to the devil everything my two hands do, if any man's lips have touched mine save yours and your cousins and mine at your command. Fie, fie," says she, " and is that all ? My love, I am happy you have told me, for I suspected it was something else; and well do I know from whom those words came. But, please God, my love, you know why he said it. By my faith, you would indeed be surprised, for he feigns to be such a friend of yours; though at heart I am glad he has roused the sleeping lion."

"And what is that?" says the goodman.

"Do not worry, my love, you shall know it another time."

"Verily," says he, "I wish to know."

"*Par Dieu*, my love," says she, "I am right wroth that you brought him here so often and let him tell you because you were so fond of him."

"Tell me," says he, "I pray you."

"*Certes*, my love, it is not fitting for you to know it."

"Tell me, for I wish to know."

Then she kisses him and caresses him most sweetly and says to him:

"Aha, my very sweet lord and lover! And would they harm me in your eyes, the false traitors?"

"Now tell me, my love, what it is."

"*Par Dieu*, my dear, whom I love above all things on earth, the traitor whom you trust, who told you those words, has urged me for more than two years to be unfaithful to you. But I have much refused him and he laboured sore in divers ways; and when you asked him to come here for love of you, he came only to betray you; nor would he leave off until I swore to him that I would tell you. But I could not bear to tell you, for he is naught to me and I am certain of myself and I would not start a quarrel between you and him, and I always thought he would desist. Alas! it is not his fault he has not put you to shame!"

"Holy Mother Mary!" says he. "He is indeed a traitor! For never did I suspect him!"

"*Par Dieu*, my lord, if he step foot in your house and I know that ever you speak to him, I shall never be at bed and board with you for, by my faith, you need have no worry about me. Please God, I shall not begin now. And I pray God, on bended knee, that the hour when that man takes me of my own free will, He would send fire down from heaven and burn me alive! Alas, my dear love," says she caressing him, "a great traitress would I be did I such wickedness or betrayed you who are so comely, so good, so tender and so gracious and who desire all I desire. May God strike me dead should I be so wanton! Moreover, my love, I desire and implore you to forbid your house to him who has accused me so treacherously, and may the devil take my soul, if he ever speak to me of it as long as I live. But, in God's name, I would not that he come again to any place where I am."

Then she falls to weeping and the goodman comforts her and promises he will do all she said, but that he will not forbid his house to the young man, who is in no wise to blame; and he swears he will never believe aught against her or listen to any man in the world. However he will never be without remorse and his heart will be a little sore. And the conclusion? His friend, who told him only for his good, will be from now on his greatest enemy. Thus is the goodman benumbed and transformed into a very beast, and through no magic. Now he has a household and is firmly caught in the trap. And the lady will do as she pleases more than ever before. And no one tells the goodman, for he will never believe it; and the one who plays the foul trick on him will be the best friend he could ever have. Old age will overtake him and perhaps he will fall into penury, from which he will never recover. This is the joy he has found in the trap of marriage! Everyone ridicules him; one man says it is a great pity, for he is a goodman; another says it does not matter, and that it is all in the rules of the game, and that he is a dull clod. Important people will reject him and will avoid his company. Thus he lives in sorrow and suffering which he takes for joys in which he will live perpetually and end his days miserably.

THE EIGHTH JOY

The eighth joy of marriage is when he, who is married, has done so much that at last he has entered into the trap wherein he has solaced himself and enjoyed all pleasure for two or three or four years, more or less; and his youthful ardour is beginning to cool and he is desirous of turning to other matters. For a man cannot always be frolicking and one cannot do the impossible. And perhaps he has had enough troubles and misfortunes aforementioned, and as a result he is greatly afflicted, so much so that he does not even dream of escape, for he is well tamed and caught in the toils. And also it may be that his wife has two or three or four children, more or less, and is big with child again; but she suffers from this pregnancy more than from all the others, wherefore the goodman is sorely worried and in great anxiety as to what will please her. Then comes the time for her lying-in and she is so ill it is a marvel, and the gossips are greatly afraid she will not recover; but the goodman makes vows to all the saints; and she, too, makes a vow to Our Lady of Puy in Auvergne, at Rochemadour and in several other places. Then it comes to pass that they hear the goodman's prayers and his wife is delivered of as fine a child as were he the Dauphin of France; and she prolongs her confinement. Her gossips come and make a splendid feast after her churching. Thus it happens that three or four of her gossips disport themselves at the house of one of their number, amusing themselves and babbling about their affairs, and perhaps there will be some farrago of which I say naught, in which they consume and destroy more goods at that merrymaking than the goodman has in eight days for his entire household.

Spring approaches and the virtues are stirred by the influence of the elements and the planets. Now is the time to frolic in the fields. Then they decide to go on a pilgrimage; and no matter what business their husbands must attend to, it is

all the same to them. Then the lady of whom we are speaking says:

"Verily, my gossip, I know not how I may leave."

"On that score I have no worry. *Par Dieu*, my gossip," says the other, "We shall all go and we shall amuse ourselves well; and my gossip so and so will come and my cousin so and so" — who, perhaps, is not her cousin at all, but only in manner of speaking. And they decide to go on a journey because they cannot do as they would in their own homes.

Then they set out on the journey and they all depart together. The lady of whom we are speaking goes to her house and wears a sour expression and the goodman comes from the town or wherever he has his business and asks her what the matter is.

"Sir," says she, "I am vexed for the child is too ill" (though in truth it is very healthy). "He is marvelous hot," says she, "and the nurse told me that for two days he would not nurse; but she dared not say so."

The goodman is deeply grieved and goes to look at the child and tears of pity come to his eyes. Night falls and when they are alone, the lady sighs and says:

"Verily, my love, you have neglected me."

"How so?" says he.

"Do you not remember," says she, "how sick I was at the birth of our child and that I made a vow to Our Lady of Puy and Rochemadour: and you have done nothing about it?"

"Forsooth, my love," says he, "Know you not how much I have to do that I know not which way to turn? But it is not too late now."

"*Par Dieu*," says she, "I shall never be happy till I have acquitted myself of it; and by my faith, it is my belief that the child is ill because of the sin I have committed."

"My love," says he, "God well knows our intentions."

"Aha!" says she, "Do not speak to me anymore; for I shall certainly go if it please God and you. And also my mother and my gossip so and so and my cousin so and so will come.

Furthermore, I would rather be the one to suffer." But whatsoever she may say, if anyone is to suffer it will be the husband and not she.

The goodman thinks on that journey and perhaps he does not have what he needs for it and is in sore distress. Then, as Quasimodo (the first Sunday after Lent) draws near, it is time to set out and he must find money to buy horses, according to his estate, and she must have a riding gown. And perhaps a certain gallant will go in the company and he will do her pleasure and service on the way, of his wealth and of his courtesy. And perhaps the goodman will also go with her; but if he goes, it were better for him, no matter what his condition, that he had remained at home, for now he must wear a millstone about his neck day in and day out. For perhaps he has no varlet and he is obliged to do many services for her on the way; and had he twenty servants they would not be enough. Moreover she would not be content unless he had worry and trouble beyond measure. Now she says that one stirrup is too long and the other too short; now she must have on her cloak; now she takes it off. Now she says the horse trots too hard and it makes her ill; now she dismounts and then she must mount again, and he is obliged to lead her horse by the bridle across a bridge or along a rough road. Now she cannot, eat and the poor man, who is more covered with mud than a dog, is forced to trot around the town in search of what she desires. And this notwithstanding, she is impatient of all things. And, moreover, the other women of their company speak to the goodman as follows:

" Verily, sir, you are not the right man to lead women on the highroad, for you can do nothing they need."

The goodman listens to them and says nothing, for he is as accustomed to quarrels and hard work as gutters are to rain. Then they arrive at Puy in Auvergne with some difficulty and make their pilgrimages, and God knows how the goodman has to push and shove in the press to get his wife through. Then she must give him her girdle and her rosary to touch to the relics and to the holy

Image of Our Lady; and God knows how he is elbowed and shoved and buffeted about. Then some rich ladies, demoiselles, and citizens' wives in their company buy rosaries of coral or jade or amber or emeralds or other jewels. Then his wife must have one as good as the others; and perhaps the goodman has not too many resources, but nonetheless he must give her one.

Then they come home and such suffering as the goodman had in going, he will have on the way home. And it may be that one of his horses can go no farther or will have an accident of a cold or of his paces or something else, and the goodman has to buy another, and perhaps he does not have the money; wherefore he will have to trot along on foot and he will always have to be near at hand. And moreover she often asks him for plums from the hedges, cherries or pears, and always gives him trouble; and first she will drop her whip or her ring or something else for him to pick up and give her.

So they return home and the goodman has need of rest; but again there is no time, for the lady, who is weary, will do naught for fifteen days save chatter with her gossips and cousins of the mountains and the beautiful things she has seen and of all that befell her. And in particular she complains of the goodman, saying that he did her no service and that she is utterly bored thereby. And the goodman finds the household at odds and ends; and he labours sore to set it right, which is not a good thing and, in short, he has all the trouble. And if there is any good, she will say it is due to her because of her good management. And if things do not go well, she will scold and say it is his fault. Henceforth she will wish to travel and be on the highroad now that she has once begun. His affairs will go wrong. He will grow old and become gouty; the household will increase and so will the expenses. Henceforth she will say that she is worn out with children and journeys and she will continue to scold and rule the household. So there is the goodman firmly caught in the trap, with sufferings and groans which he deems to be joys. There he is and will always remain and will end his days miserably.

THE NINTH JOY

The ninth joy of marriage is when the young man has put himself into the trap and the prison of matrimony and, after the pleasure they found in it at first, the wife will perhaps be temperamental and ill-natured (and they are all like that) and always seeks to have as much authority and power in the house as her husband — or more if she can. But it may be that he is a prudent and spiteful man and will not suffer it but, has resisted in numerous ways and many and many a time there have been disputes and arguments between them and sometimes even fights. But however that may be, and notwithstanding all the wars that have been waged between them for twenty or thirty years or more, he has remained in control of his possessions. And you can imagine that, in so long a time, he has had much to suffer; for perchance he has had many of the adversities and tribulations we have already mentioned and those that are hereinafter related. Nonetheless he has remained victorious and has not been forcibly insulted or dishonoured but has had to suffer much, as you may well imagine. And perhaps he has had pretty daughters whom he has married well. Thus it happens that, because of the great trials and tribulations, the bad nights and the cold he has suffered in his efforts to build up his resources and live honourably, as every man must, that, either through worries or through old age, the goodman languishes and falls ill, with gout or something else, and to such an extent that he cannot get up from his chair or move from one place to another; or he has something the matter with a leg or an arm, or suffers some of those accidents that happen to many people. Then the war is over and luck has gone against him. For the lady, who is lively and perhaps younger than he, will now do only as she pleases. The goodman, who has waged war on many planes, is caught. From now on the children, whom the goodman had caused to be well instructed and kept on a short rein, will be poorly taught. And if the good man scolds them, the lady will side against him; wherefore his heart will be heavy with sorrow. And moreover he is dependent upon his servants for the many services he has need of. And though his mind is just as good as ever, they make him think he is senile because he is unable to move without help. And perhaps his oldest son wishes to take control of the property and his mother backs him, as if he could not wait for his father to die — and there are many like him. And thus the goodman sees that he is overruled and that his wife, his children and his servants neglect him and do not do his commands. And it may even be that they do not want him to make a will for fear he will not give his wife what she asks of him; and sometimes they leave him in his bedchamber for half a day and do not go near him and he suffers hunger and thirst and cold. Wherefore the goodman, who has been prudent and wise and still has very good sense, is thrown into great despair of mind and says to himself that he will look into this and he sends for his wife and his children. For perhaps the wife, for her comfort, has ceased to sleep with him for the poor man can do nothing but moan and groan. Alas! All the pleasures he once gave his wife are forgotten, but she remembers the quarrels and tells her neighbors he has been a harsh man and has led her such a cruel life that, had she not been a woman of great patience, she could not have continued to live with him. And what is worse, she often tells the goodman that his sins will work against him. And perhaps she is an old bag, skinny and argumentative, and she revenges herself thus on him because she has not been able to rule him in times past, for he was a wise and prudent man. And you can imagine how glad the good man is to be thus reproved!! And when the lady and her children come before him, as we have said, he says to his wife:

"My dear," says he, "you are the one in the world I should love most, and you should love me. And know that I am not pleased with many things that are done to me. You know that I am master of the house and will be so as long as I live, but no one acts as if I were. And were I a poor man obliged to beg for his bread, they would not dare to treat me as I am now treated. You know, my dear, that I have loved and cherished you and have labored sore to maintain our estate; and your children and mine treat me ill."

"And what do you expect me to do?" says the lady. "We do the best we can for you, and you always keep asking for more. But the more one does for you, the worse you are, nor were you ever otherwise: I know whereof I speak."

"Aha, fair lady, hold your tongue! For I have nothing more to do with you." The goodman addresses his eldest son.

"Listen to me, my good son; I see what you are doing and I am not pleased. You are my eldest son and will be my principle heir, if you conduct yourself well. But I note that you have assumed authority and taken over the conduct of my property. Do not make so bold, but think instead of serving me and obeying me as you should. I have been a good father to you for I have not wasted my patrimony, but have added to it and have amassed good property for you. For if you go against my wishes, I swear on my word of honour that you will regret it and you will never enjoy what God gave me. And thus I warn you."

"And what would you have him do?" asks the lady. "We cannot tell how to serve you. For he who would be ever at your beck and call would have too much to do; and you and I would be in paradise and, in future, that would not be a great pity. You do not know what you ask. Are you not confortable?"

"Then, fair lady," says he, "hold your tongue and do not encourage him, for that is ever your way."

Then they leave, and the lady and her son confer together and they say he is senile. Wherefore, because he has threatened his son, they say he is on the way to wreck his inheritance which will not be provided for and they decide that no man in the world shall ever talk with him again. The son will take control more than ever before, for the mother supports him. They go away and tell everyone that the good man has reverted to his childhood; and the son labours to have the goodman put under guardianship. And they make him believe he has lost his senses and his memory, though he is as sane as ever he was. And if someone comes to the house to speak to him who was wont to keep a good house and make good cheer to people who came to see him, and they ask the lady for the goodman, she will say:

"By my troth, my friends, he is in the hospital."

"And what," says he, "has happened to him?"

"By my troth," says she, "he is like a babe and has lately gone back to his childhood. God be praised," says she, "for what He gives me, for I am sore burdened with heavy household cares and have no one to attend to it but me."

"Verily," says he, "that is a great pity and it surprises me greatly, for I have seldom seen such a wise man as he in all the land."

"God's will be done," says she.

Thus is the goodman ruled, who has lived honourably and conducted himself and his household well, as you may believe. Now you may imagine that the goodman wears out his life in great languishing, for he cannot move from any place and cannot go an tell the grave wrongs they are doing to him. Thus he languishes and wastes his life. Never will he have any joy and it is a marvel that he is not plunged into despair as well he would be, were he not a wise man. Thus he must be patient for he has no other choice; nor will anyone speak to him save to take leave of him. And as for me, I believe that this is one of the great sorrows on earth. Thus the goodman does penance and often weeps over his sins in the trap he has so greatly desired and had laboured sore to enter and from which he will never come out. And if he were not in it, he would never stop till he had got in. And thus he will remain, languishing perpetually, and end his days in misery.

THE TENTH JOY

The tenth joy of marriage is when he, who is to marry, has put himself in the trap because he has seen other fish disporting themselves gaily inside - or so itseems to him; and he has laboured sore till he found the entrance and could be at his pleasures and delights, as we have said. And one may say he has been lured into the trap of marriage as the hunter lures wild ducks into the pond by means of certain trained birds or decoys, and gives them corn to eat; and the wild birds, who do naught but fly from river to river in search of food that pleases them, imagine themselves to be very happy. Alack! they are not; for each of them is held by the foot and they are brought home in a basket one on top of the other in great suffering, which is contrary to their nature. Many of the poor birds would be happy if they were free like the others who can go from river to river and taste all sorts of food. But when they see the others feeding, as we have said, they join them in great flocks and in great haste, one ahead of the other, with the exception of some shrewd birds who have seen and heard of the pond and have not forgotten it, and have been afraid of it and have drawn back from it as from fire. For the poor birds who are in it have lost their freedom and will never recover it, but will remain perpetually in slavery. And what is worse, their days are shortened. Nonetheless he, who is to marry, of whom we are speaking, has seen to it that he runs the least possible danger; or perhaps he does so without taking any precautions at all. Wherefore he imagines he is having joys, delights and frolickings where he has put himself; but he has found quite the opposite. And it sometimes happens, by I know not what means, that he is told that those are magic rites, hoodoos or evil spells, that his wife will never love him; and she tells this to her cousin or to her mother, who warn her when she lies with her husband and her flesh prickles like needles, never to make love nor to give her husband pleasure. And she says also that he can do nothing save when it pleases the Fates, no matter what good will they have. This, it seems to me, is a very great torment; as one who might have great thirst and holds his mouth to water and cannot drink. And it often happens that such women, in that condition, have a lover and when they are together, he is not under an evil spell, but enjoys himself well and helps her to enjoy herself.

Thus it often happens that, either because of his wife's carelessness or her paramour's, the husband becomes aware of it and beats her. And sometimes she deliberately sets out to betray him — which has happened to a number of men. And sometimes, perhaps, because of the ugly rows he makes and also because he beats her, she deserts her husband and goes on a journey. Nonetheless some husbands worry and search and enquire on all sides and would give all their chattels if they could find her. And when she has amused herself well with her paramour and sees her husband's good will, she has some of her friends persuade her mother to say that she has been with her all the time and that the poor girl went away because he had hurt her. "I would rather," says the mother to the husband, "that you would send her back to me altogether than to beat her that way; for well do I know that my daughter never did aught against you," and she makes him swear a great oath.

"Now look," says she, "if she did not behave well, it would be your fault if she were lost. And know that it has happened to some to be lost to all shame for the sake of wearing the breeches or for other things worse."

Sometimes, perhaps, the man or the woman asks for a separation; sometimes the husband accuses the wife and the wife accuses the husband. They have put themselves into the trap and they want to get outside; but it is too late to repent. They plead bitterly. And sometimes, mayhap, because they do not produce sufficient cause for a separation or do not sufficiently prove their intention, the judge sentences them to remain married and he admonishes them. Now in addition to the situation in which they were at first, they have this bit more, for they were not happy; and moreover they have made themselves the laughing-stock of all. Sometimes, perhaps, they produce sufficient causes, one against the other; wherefore the judge sentences them to separate and orders them, under heavy penalty, to keep themselves chaste and continent. But this is what happens; one or the other, or both, act foolishly and do as they wish wherever they please. Sometimes a certain woman will go from bedchamber to bedchamber in a good city and have her pleasure. They think they have put themselves outside the trap and that they have escaped; but they are worse off than before. Then the man is ruined, according to his degree, and lost in this world, and the woman too; neither the one nor the other can marry all their lives long. If they have great possessions and are from a great place, their name is ruined and they will die without heirs. The man is greatly ashamed of his wife who has frolicked vulgarly; for perhaps some gallant is shamefully keeping her in his house. And it seems to me that this is one of the greatest torments that man can have. Then what a marriage he has! Thus he wears out his life in the trap, in suffering and tribulation, where he will live languishing always and end his days miserably.

THE ELEVENTH JOY

The eleventh joy of marriage is when a young and merry gallant rides gaily through the country and is free from all restraint and may go from place to place as it pleases him. And throughout the year he goes to many places, particularly where he knows ladies, demoiselles, citizens' wives and other women, according to his degree; and because he is young, lusty, pleasing and amorous, and is still forthright and inexperienced, he gives heed only to seeking his pleasures and delights. Perhaps he has a father and a mother or one or the other to whom he is all their joy and they have no other child but him and therefore they mount and dress him well. Or perhaps he is recently lord of the estate and goes blithely through the land in good companies and in good places; and if he finds a lady, demoiselle, citizens' wife or others, who would have to do with him, he would fall to willingly.

And he comes to a house where there is a beautiful demoiselle who is perhaps of higher degree than he, or perhaps lesser, or is a bourgeoise or of some other degree; but be that as it may, she is beautiful and honest and so gracious in her ways that it is a marvel to behold. And because she is so beautiful and so well renowned, she has been prized and courted and more supplicants have come there. And perchance there have been so many, and one among them has pressed his suit so vigorously that she has been unable to refuse. For a sensitive woman of sanguine disposition is free and gay and would never refuse a plea, if the one who makes it pursues her sufficiently and in the right way; though other women of various dispositions pay good heed to reason if there be one to explain matters to them. But let us return to the young demoiselle who has listened to the importunities and pleas of a poor companion who has several times told her his complaints and she has granted him what he asked; and perhaps she is the daughter of the house, the niece or a relative, and has gone so far that she is big with child — for which there is no remedy save to hide it and repair the wrong as best one can. And thus the lady who knows about it and is a fairly wise woman, will make good provision, God willing; and the poor man who has done this is banished and never comes back. Or the lady might arrange so well that he would take the demoiselle to wife; but perhaps he is a poor clerk or of other degree, and they will not give her to him; or perhaps he is married, which often happens. And sometimes God punishes married men for like torments; for they betray their wives, which is folly, for they do not know what they are doing. For the wife who feels herself outraged is of poor mettle if she does not try to take her revenge.

The poor girl, who is big with child, must take what has come and she has not much time, and she herself knows nothing about it for she is but a child and does not know what it is. But the lady, who knows plenty of things, has clearly recognized it, for the poor girl vomits in the morning and turns pale. Then the lady, who knows the Old Testament and the New, bethinks herself and calls the girl to her secretly.

" Come here," says she. " I told you before, you are ruined and dishonoured to have done what you have done. But what is done is done. Well do I know you are big with child. Now tell me the truth."

" By my troth," says the young girl who is but a tender young thing between fifteen and seventeen years of age and just beginning to live, " Madam, I know nothing."

" It seems to me," says the lady, " that when morning comes I see you vomit and make such and such a face."

" Verily, Madam," says she, " it is true that I am sick."

" Aha ! " says the lady, " you are with child and no mistake ! Do not say a word and do not let anyone in the world know ! And take heed that you do as I shall tell you."

" Gladly, Madam," says the child.

" Have you not seen," says the lady, " such and such a knight who comes here often ? "

" Yes, verily, Madam."

" Then pay good heed, for he will come to-morrow. And see that you give him good welcome and in good style. And when you see that I and the other fine ladies and gentlemen are talking together, cast your eyes upon him very sweetly, in good manner and do thus." Then she shows her what she must do. " And if he speaks to you, listen to him readily and sweetly and reply to him very courteously. And if he begs for your love, listen to him well and thank him, but say that you do not know what that is and that moreover, you do not wish to know. For whatever one may say, she is a wise woman who will not listen to men who would pleasure her. And if he would give you gold or money, do not take any. And if he offers you a ring, a girdle or other things, refuse them gently; but in the end take them for love of him, and without thought of evil or insult. And when he is about to take his leave, ask him if it will be long ere one sees him again."

" Gladly, Madam," says the demoiselle.

Then the charming gallant, who is to be caught in the trap, arrives; for the lady would marry him to the demoiselle, if she can, for he has a good inheritance and is naive and inexperienced. Then he comes to see the demoiselles, for he is over-confident; he is given good cheer for they have all laid their snares to trap him. They go to dine and he fares sumptuously. After dinner, the lady takes a cavalier or a knight and sits down and the others sit down to talk and amuse themselves. The gallant remains standing near the young girl and they converse together; and perhaps he steps forward and takes her by the hand and says to her:

" Would to God, my demoiselle, you knew my thoughts! "

" Your thoughts? " says she. " And how could I know them if you do not tell me what they are? Are you thinking," says she, " things you should not tell me? "

" Faith," says he, "No, I am thinking nothing I would not have you know. But I would that

you knew my thoughts without my telling them to you."

"Verily," says she, laughing, "You say things one should not say."

"If you wish," says he, "in order not to displease you, I will tell you."

"Sir," says she, "say what you please, for well do I know that you will tell me only good."

"Lady," says he, "I am a poor knight and well do I know I am unworthy to be your lover, for you are beautiful and sweet and gracious and full of all the good things Nature ever bestowed on a young girl; but if it pleased you to honour me, I would venture to boast of good will, diligence and all the services man could do, for I will serve you and never leave you, come what may, and I will guard your honour above mine own."

"I thank you, sir, but, forsooth, do not speak to me of such things, for I do not know what it is nor do I wish to know. For that is not what Madam teaches me every day."

"Faith," says he, "my demoiselle! Madam, of

whom you speak, is a very good lady; but she would know naught, if you so desire, for I should be guided solely by your wishes."

"But, my good sir, I heard the other day that you were to be married. Much astounded am I that you come and speak such words?"

"Faith, my demoiselle, if you please, I shall never marry as long as it pleases you for me to be your servitor."

"That will never be," says she, "to your advantage or to mine. And your friends would not advise it. And, moreover, would you really wish me to be dishonoured?"

"Faith," says he, "my demoiselle, I would rather be dead."

"*Par Dieu*," says she, "be silent, for if Madam should notice I would be lost."

And perhaps the lady has made her a sign to desist, for she fears the demoiselle will not play her part well. Then surreptitiously he gives her a ring or something else and says to her: "I pray you, my demoiselle, keep this for love of me."

"*Certes*," says she, "I will not take it."

"Alas!" says he, "my demoiselle, I implore you to."

He puts it in her hand and she takes it and says:

"I shall take it therefore for love of you and in all honour, thinking no ill of it."

Then the lady says to the gentlemen, some of whom are perhaps relatives of the young girl:

"Tomorrow we must go on a pilgrimage to Notre Dame in such a place."

"Verily," say they, "Madam has well said."

They go to supper and the gallant always stands near the demoiselle who continues to play her part so well that he is all aflame with love, for a young man in such a state does not know what he is doing.

Then comes the next day when they mount their horses and the only horse to carry pillion, they all say, is that of the gallant, wherefore he has great joy for they give him the demoiselle up behind him. She puts her arms around him to keep her balance and God only knows how happy he is, for he would have given a vast portion of his land to hold her at his pleasure. Now he is close to entering into the trap. Then they make their journey in deep devotion, God knows. They return to the house to dine, for the journey has been made only to ensnare the young man. The gallant is constantly beside the young girl. After dinner the lady goes to her chamber and says to the girl:

" Come, tell me how you have managed."

" By my troth, Madam," says she, " he never ceased imploring me all day long." And she tells her everything.

" Then go on," says she, " Answer him very sweetly and tell him we are thinking of giving you in marriage, but that you do not wish to be married yet. And if he offers to take you, thank him and tell him you will speak to me about it and that he is the one man in the world you could love most."

Then they all go into the garden and wander through the paths and trails and the gallant says to the girl:

" My love, take pity on me."

" Alas," says she, " I pray you, do not speak of

it anymore or I shall leave your company. Would you have me lose my honour ? " says she. " Have you not heard that there is talk of marrying me ? "

" By my soul," says he, " I would not decry anyone, but it is my belief that I am as able to serve you and please you as he of whom I have heard talk."

" Faith," says she, " well do I know that you are better and would indeed that he resembled you."

" I thank you, my demoiselle," says he, " well do I see from your courtesy that you prize me higher than I deserve, but if it please you to do me the honour, I would deem myself highly honoured."

" Many thanks, sir," says she. " I shall have to speak to Madam and to my friends."

" If I knew they would be pleased to hear me," says he, " I would speak to them."

" Forsooth," says she, " do not say you have mentioned it to me, nor that I have discussed it with you, for I would die."

" I shall not do so," says he.

He goes off at once and speaks to the lady most humbly, for he has great fear lest she refuse him. In short, so well is the secret kept that they become engaged or otherwise take matters into their own hands without a word to any man, which frequently happens, and perchance they are allowed to sleep together. The poor man is in the trap and has married without telling father or mother who are wondrous grieved. For they know it is not the marriage for him and have heard enough about it and are crushed. They are married without banns and without formalities, for he is in haste to possess her, and moreover the demoiselle's friends are afraid lest there be some impediment. Night comes and know that the mother has trained her daughter well and has taught her to comport herself in a manner befitting a virgin with many cries and gasps like a person who is suddenly plunged naked into cold water and is not accustomed to it. This she does and plays her part to good effect for he is not wise to the ways of a woman in private matters.

All goes well until the next meeting; but now see what happens! The father and mother are so angry that it is a marvel to behold; nonetheless pity and love for their child make them receive the gallant and his wife. But now see the greater trouble that comes to pass, for the poor wife has been carrying a child for two, three or four months and can no longer hide it. Then all the joys of times past are turned to sorrows. For he is such that he will put her out and will be ashamed and such a one will know it who would not have known anything; and she will not be able to marry again; and know that she will not spare herself. And if he keeps her, she will never love him, nor he her, and she will help herself to everything she can. On the other hand, he will remind her frequently of what she has done, and perhaps he will beat her and never will they have a happy marriage. Nonetheless he is in the trap from which he will never escape, but there he will languish always and end his days miserably.

THE TWELFTH JOY

The twelfth joy of marriage is when the young man has gone to and fro so much that he has found the entrance into the trap and has entered into it and has found the very wife he longed for. And perhaps it would have been better for him to have found another, but not for anything would he have her. For it seems to him he is better off than any man and he is happy it pleased God for him to find her for, in his opinion, there is none to equal her. And he listens to her words and is proud of her achievements and her discretion, though perhaps she does not know that she is daydreaming. And it may be that the goodman is all disposed to do her bidding and is governed by her advice. And when anyone has business with him, he says: " I shall speak to my wife or to the lady of our house." And if she approves, he will do it: and if she disapproves, he will do nothing. For the goodman is so tamed that he is as lively as an ox at the plow. Now he is done for. If he is a noble and the prince calls him to his army, he will go, if the lady so desires. And he may say:

"My love, I must go to the army."

"You must go!" says she. "And what will you do there! Spend all your resources and get yourself killed? And then your children and I will be in a fine state."

In short, if it does not please her, he will not go — and let him who may, defend the country, and he who will, guard his honour. And moreover, when it pleases her, she sends him out of the house and orders him here and there to suit her whim. If she quarrels, he says not a word, for no matter how wrong she may be, he always thinks she is right and that she is a wise woman. From now on he will do great things, for he is under his wife's thumb. For when it comes to understanding, the wisest woman in the world has no more than I have gold in my eye or an ape has tail; for understanding fails her before she is half way through what she would do or say. And if things are thus, the goodman has trouble enough to endure and, if she is a good woman, he bears with her actions; and if she is otherwise, as frequently happens, think how much he has to suffer and how she fools him and imposes upon him. Now she sends him to bed when he would stay awake. And if she has some private matters to attend to, she makes him get up at midnight and reminds him of a task he must do or sends him on a pilgrimage to which she had vowed herself, in great haste, because she has a pain in her side, and he shall go, rain or hail. And if perchance the gallant, her lover, who knows the entrances into the house, would speak with her and cannot wait till nightfall, he enters the house and hides in the cellar or in the stable to find means to speak to the lady; or perhaps he is so desperate that he will enter the same chamber where the husband lies sleeping. For a lustful reprobate grows desperate and will do whatever his lust bids to accomplish his desire. Thus it often happens that many, because of their reprehensible behavior, are seen or discovered, whereby their ladies are defamed even though they are so free and uninhibited that when they see the pains their lovers go to for their sakes, they would never refuse them, even were they to die for it; but, instead, the fires of love flame higher. And sometimes when the gallant rushes into the house, as I have said, the dog hears him and barks, but she makes the husband think it is rats and that she has often seen the dog behave thus. And even were the goodman to see her misdeed plainly, he would not believe it but would think she was doing something to aid him. In short, he is firmly caught in the trap. She has the children brought to him to play with, she makes him rock them and has him hold her spindle when she spins on a Saturday.

But his business is poor and a new anxiety faces him, for war comes to the country wherefore every man draws back into towns and castles. But the goodman cannot go away and leave his wife, and perhaps he is caught and taken prisoner dishonourably and is beaten and pays a heavy ransom. Now he has to look out for himself and, to avoid being caught, he flees to a castle. But by night he comes to his house, feeling his way through woods, between hedges and thickets till he is all worn out and scratched and cut; and he comes to his house and the lady weeps and scolds and pours out all the bad news and trouble, as if he could make peace between the Kings of France and England, and she says she will not stay there. So the goodman is obliged to carry his wife and children in great haste to the castle or to the town; and God only knows the trouble he has to mount the lady and the children, to pack bags and clothes and to lodge them when they are in the fortress; no man can really describe it. But you may imagine what trouble he has and how thin he becomes and how tormented by quarrels; for she knows not where to take revenge for her misfortune, if not on him who must suffer great hardships in wind and rain. And now he must trot by day, now by night, on foot or on horseback, according to his estate, to seek food for her and attend to her other needs. In short, his poor body will never rest, but will have naught but pain and tribulation for he is made for nothing else. And if it came to pass that, because of his wrath at his wife's scolding, he is so weighed down with trouble that he refuses to answer her or otherwise, his woes will be redoubled, for he will be vanquished in the end and will be more downtrodden than ever; for it is now too late to rebel. You must know that the children are badly raised and poorly taught, and the goodman dare not touch them, and they must have everything they ask for; and whatever they do is well done, even were they to knock out their father's eye with a stone while playing. Then when the war is over he must transport them all back home and the trouble begins all over again. Then the husband grows old and will be less esteemed than before and will be cast off like an old falconer that is good for naught. The lady marries her daughters as she pleases and sometimes the husbands are worthless; and neither the daughters nor their husbands think highly of the goodman who has the gout and cannot aid himself because of

all the ills he suffers. Then does the goodman weep for his sins in the trap in which he is held fast and from which he will never escape; and he dare not buy a mass or make a will or else he puts his soul in his wife's hands. Thus he wastes his life in languishing and sorrow and there he will remain ever and end his days miserably.

THE THIRTEENTH JOY

The thirteenth joy of marriage is when he who has married, has lived with his wife five or six years or more, and has been so happy that it seems to him he has found a very good and chaste wife and thus, perhaps, has lived with her in great pleasure and delight. And he is a nobleman and desires to gain honours and rewards and would go out into the world. And when he says this to his wife, she kisses and caresses him and tells him many times, sighing and weeping:

"Alas, my love, would you leave me and go away from me? And would you leave your children and we would not know if we would ever see you again?" And day and night she does her best to detain him and keep him from going.

"My sweet," says he, "I must go for my honour and because I must obey the king or I shall lose the fief I hold from him; but, if it please God, I shall see you very soon."

Perhaps he goes overseas in some army to win honours and knighthood; for there are sometimes men so brave and so noble of heart that neither love of wife or children will hold them back from honourable deeds. Thus he takes leave of his wife with great regret, and the latter grieves and mourns exceedingly; but he is a man who loves honor and, as we have said, nothing can hold him back.

Many men, however, cannot go ten or twelve leagues from their wives to defend their country and themselves, save under constraint, which is, without doubt, a great shame to all nobles; and they are weak and should be deprived of all good company and of the name and privileges of nobles, though no-one who hears of this would maintain that such men are noble even if their fathers were.

Let us return then to that nobleman of whom we are speaking. He goes away and commends his wife and his children, whom he loves more than anything after his honour, to his special friends. Then it may be that he sails across the sea and is captured by the enemy where, by luck or otherwise, he remains two or three or four years or more and cannot come home. The lady is in great grief for a time and perhaps she hears that he is dead and she mourns him so greatly that it is a marvel. But she cannot weep always and she grows calm, thank God, and to such an extent that she marries again and takes her pleasure and soon forgets her husband whom she was wont to love so dearly. And her love for her children is forgotten; the smiling countenance, the caresses, the kisses she was wont to give her husband are all forgotten, and anyone who would see her with her present husband would say she loves him more than she did the other who is a prisoner or in other affliction because of his valour. His children, whom the goodman loved, are cast aside and their portion is spent. So they frolic and amuse themselves and enjoy each other. Then, perchance, the good nobleman, her husband, comes home and he is greatly aged and wasted, for he has not been in comfort these two or three or four years he has been a prisoner. And when he comes to his native land, he enquires for his wife and his children. For greatly does he fear they may be dead or in need, which thoughts the goodman has had many a time in prison and has had many worries while his wife was enjoying herself. Perhaps at the very hour when the goodman was thinking such thoughts and praying God to guard his wife and children from evil, the husband she had recently wed was holding her in his arms. Then the goodman learns she has married. Now judge how keen his sorrow on hearing such news! I believe that neither the grief of the great King Priam of Troy when told of the death of Hector the Brave, nor the grief of Jacob at the death of his son Joseph, could equal this grief. Than he comes home and knows the thing to be true. If he is a man of honour, never will he take her; and the other man, who has taken her and enjoyed her, will leave her. And thus is she lost to honour and perhaps will start on the downward path to such a degree that the goodman will suffer constant grief thereof and never will he forget. His children likewise will be shamed by their mother's wrongdoing. Neither husband nor wife will be able to marry again during the other's lifetime. And it has happened in the past that, because of his wife's urging, a husband who is of high and noble courage, fights on the field of honour; and sometimes, as luck will have it, he is conquered and killed shamefully, which is a great sorrow. Many a time it happens that he who is in the right is defeated, and he who is in the wrong is victorious. And it has sometimes come to pass that, because of his wife's pride and vanity, the husband takes umbrage with another man, as powerful or more so than he, for the precedence of their wives in church and their turn to receive the paten, and they argue and fight, for each would go before the other. And they stir up perpetual trouble between them and they gather their friends together and demand great estate of their wives that each may outdo the other and they spend their resources wildly; wherefore they sometimes sell their chattels or their lands and are reduced to penury. And for this, those to whom the aforesaid things have happened thought to find allurement in the trap of marriage into which they sought to enter in search of comfort; but they have found just the contrary, though that is not what they think. Thus they waste their lives in suffering in which they will remain always and will end their days miserably.

THE FOURTEENTH JOY

The fourteenth joy of marriage is when the young man has done his best to find the entrance into the trap, and he has entered into it and has found a beautiful young wife, sweet and gracious, artless, pleasant and gay. And they have enjoyed great delights and pleasures for two or three years and have done nothing to displease either the one or the other, but have given each other all the pleasures man can think of, with never a quarrel between them, the two of them billing and cooing like two turtle doves. For they two are one and Nature has endowed them with so much sweetness that if one of them fell ill, the other would do likewise. And this comes to pass when they are in the first flush of youth. But it may happen that the lady departs this life, wherefore the young man suffers such grief as no man can ever imagine. Now his luck has changed, for it is not reasonable that people who are in prison should live for their pleasures; for were that so, it would not be a prison. The young man falls into great despair: now he finds fault with God, now with death, now with Fortune that has pursued him as if to take all his joy from him; and it seems to me that this is as great sorrow as any we have related above.

Thus he lives for a time in misery and in tribulation of thought and keeps to himself, avoiding companions and dwelling constantly on the great loss he has suffered. And ever before him he sees the face of his wife whom he loved so dearly. But there is nothing in this world that does not come to an end. Thus there are some people in the city or in the country who say he is a good man and honest and a person of substance, and they do their best to get him married. And they marry him to another lady who is, in every way, the opposite of his former wife. And she has been married before and is not one of those lovely young girls, but is a woman of a certain age and knows many things, for she has learned from her first husband how to manage the second. She weighs the situation and deals with it wisely and is slow to show her cunning. But when she sees that he is ingenuous and debonnaire and when she knows him and his circumstances, she displays and unleashes all the malice in her box. She seizes authority and would rule him and make him suffer many pains and torments. For there is no greater slave in the worst bondage than a naive and goodnatured young man who is subject to, and under the thumb of, a widow woman, and the more so when she is ill-tempered and capricious. He is well advised to pretend to yield, for the woman who has come to this pass is like a cruel and pitiless rogue, chosen to punish felons. And for the man who falls into this pass there is no help but to pray God to give him patience to endure and suffer all, like an old toothless bear, fettered with a great iron chain, muzzled, and fastened to a huge wooden bar, whose only revenge is to roar, and every time he roars he is given two or three blows more.

To this may be likened the ingenuous goodman

who has married a shrewish and temperamental widow. And it often happens that, because he is so much younger, she becomes jealous. For the delight and pleasure of young flesh has made her greedy and jealous, and she would have him always in her arms and would be constantly near him. She is like the fish in a stream where, because of the strength of the great summer's heat which has lasted a long time, the water ceases to flow and becomes stagnant; wherefore the fish is desirous of finding fresh water and the moment he finds it he goes up the stream. The same does the woman of a certain age when she finds a young man and young flesh that renews her. And know that there is nothing so displeasing to a young man as an old woman, and nothing more harmful to his health. He is like a man who drinks musty wine. As long as he is drinking and is thirsty, it will do. But when he has drunk, he has a bad after-taste and will not drink again unless he finds another wine. So it is with the young man who has an old wife, for certainly he will never love her, and even less will a young

woman love an old man. And there are some men who, out of avarice, marry old women; but those women are foolish no matter what services the young men render them; for they will never keep the promises they have made. And I consider even more foolish an old man who tries to play the gallant and marries a young woman. When I see such things, I laugh to myself when I think how they will end. For know that if an old man takes a young woman, it will be great luck if she turns to him to fulfill her desires. And think how she, who is young and tender and sweet of breath, can endure the old man who coughs, spits, sneezes, and complains all night long — not to mention other things—so that it is a marvel she does not kill herself. And his breath is foul because of his liver trouble or other hazards that old people suffer. And moreover the one will be contrary to the pleasure of the other. Now consider if it is well to put two contrary things together? It is like putting a cat and a dog in the same sack: they will always fight to the very end. Thus it sometimes happens that the man and the woman take what they need and spend their goods so extravagantly that many are reduced to poverty. And it often happens that such old people become jealous and more greedy than others; and the matter will go from bad to worse, for if he were once young it will be all the worse. And when the gallants see a pretty young girl married to an old man or to a young fool and they see that she is merry and debonnaire, they are on the alert; for rightly do they think she will listen to them more readily than would a girl who has a young and able husband. And when an old woman marries a young man, the young man consents only out of avarice; wherefore never will he love her; and such young men beat the old wives and put their money to bad use and sometimes are reduced to penury. And know that to frequent an old woman shortens a young man's life; wherefore Hippocrates has said: NON VETULAM NOVI, CUR MORIARI ! And such old women, married to young men, are wont to be so jealous and so greedy that they are completely ravenous; and wherever the husband goes, to church or elsewhere, they think he goes only for an evil purpose; and God knows in what torment and tribulation he is and the pitched battles he has. And never would a young wife be so jealous for the aforesaid reasons; moreover she will have the remedy at hand whenever she wishes. But he, who has come to the aforesaid pass, is so bound that he dare not speak to any woman and is obliged to serve the lady who is old; wherefore he will age more in one year than he would with a young woman in ten years. The old woman will wear him out and he will continue to live in quarrels, sufferings and torments in which he will remain always and will end his days in misery.

THE FIFTEENTH JOY

The fifteenth joy of marriage which, save for death, I hold to be the greatest and most extreme suffering, is when a man, to his misfortune, has turned so often around the trap that he has found the way in and perhaps has found a wife who sports and frolics and enjoys the pleasures of the world at will. And this she has done so long that her husband finally suspects and notices it; and then come disputes and tribulations familiar to such a case. But be sure that, when it comes to enjoying herself, she will never cease, no matter how much he rages, no, not even were he to kill her, but will do exactly as she pleases.

Thus, perhaps, the husband, who is suspicious, has seen the gallant, who attends to his affairs when he is absent from home, enter his house; wherefore he falls into a passion of anguish and rage that wrings his heart. Thus, like a madman, he hastens to the bedchamber where the lovers are and finds them together — or nearly so. He tries to seize the poor reckless lover, who is so surprised he can neither speak nor defend himself. And as the husband is about to stab him, the lady, out of pity for the poor man and to do her duty (for she must ever take care to prevent murder), embraces her husband and says to him:

"Aha! Forsooth, my lord, take heed lest you do an evil deed."

At this, the gallant who has had time to catch his breath, takes to his heels and makes off and the other, who has now no time to kill his wife, goes after him. And thus the poor lover escapes him, which is all very well and not surprising; for there are none so prompt to fly, depending upon their need, as those rascals escaping from the hands of those who would catch them. Then the husband, unable to find him, returns in haste to the bedchamber to curse or kill his wife, which would be very wicked of him, for he is not certain that they had done wrong.

Now you must know that the poor woman is

in despair. She goes home to her mother, to her sister or to her cousin; but it is best for her to go to her mother. The poor woman tells her mother all that befell her; but she says that the gallant had come in by chance and that he had never been there before; and that her husband happened to find her talking with him but no harm had been done. And her mother asks:

" In the devil's name, had he aught to do with you ? " says she.

" *Par Dieu*, it is true he spoke thereof to me two or three times, but I always firmly refused him; and all he did was to come in and speak of it and I told him he must go away."

Then she swears by all the saints that she would as lief he were hanged. Or perhaps she confesses the whole affair to her; for the mother, who knows plenty about the old dance, says:

" *Certes*, I thought theres was omewhat else, nor would I ever believe he would enter your bedchamber had he not great knowledge of you. Tell me frankly," says she, " that I may seek to set things straight."

The daughter lowers her head and blushes.

" Aha! " says the mother, " Well do I know it is so. Tell me, tell me how it is! "

" Faith, the wicked man has been pressing me for more than two years and I have always defended myself well, until once when my husband was away, he entered our house (I know not how for I had locked the door) and forced me. And, by my soul, I defended myself more than half the night — and you know that I am only a poor woman alone."

" Aha! By all the devils," says the mother, " I knew it well. Now, first of all," says she, " see that you conduct yourself wisely and let the young man neither go there nor come here."

" Aha! Madam! It would take a court order to keep him away! For well do I know he is now distressed, fearing lest my husband has killed me; and so reckless is he that he will come to know whether I am dead or alive."

" I am astounded," says the mother, " that your husband did not kill him and you too."

" *Ave Maria*! Madam! I give you my word,

had I not embraced my husband, the poor young man would be dead."

"You did well to protect him, for when a poor man has risked his person to serve a woman and suffers sleepless nights as a result, it were better she were dead than to let him be scurrilously attacked."

"Alas, my lady, if you knew what manner of man he is! For, by my troth, I have seen the time when it rained and hailed and was as black as an oven and the poor man came all the way on foot that he might pass unnoticed, and waited in our garden more than half the night, for I could find no way to go to him. And when I did go, I found the poor man half frozen, but he made naught of it."

"I marvelled," says the mother, "to see what great honour he does me. When I go to church, he comes to give me holy water, and wherever he finds me, he does all manner of service he can."

"By my faith, Madam, he loves you well."

"Now first of all," says the mother, "whoever can must remedy matters. Come hither," says she to the serving-wench. "Go and say to my gossips so and so that I bid them come to me, for I have somewhat to say to them."

The serving-wench goes off and tells the gossips that the mother has sent for them. The gossips come to the house and sit around a glowing fire, if it is winter; and if it is summer, they sit on the rushes. And the first thing they do, before they even say a *Pater* or an *Ave Maria*, is to drink as much as they can, and God knows the noise they make can be heard in Anglois fifteen leagues away. Then one of the gossips says to the mother or to the daughter:

"My gossip, your daughter is not of good cheer!"

"*Par Dieu*, my gossip, she has suffered a base mishap, wherefore I have summoned you here."

Then she tells them the whole story and perhaps she does not tell it exactly as it is; or perhaps she will tell them the whole truth, because some of them have been in the same situation and will be able to give better advice. And well do the others know what such experiences are and what they mean, but so well have they managed their affairs, and so secretly, that there has been no scandal, God be thanked! Then they consult together and each gives her opinion and tells how she conducted herself in like case; which is a fine pretext for citing a case they have seen come to pass and experienced. Some find fault, others answer back and others talk among themselves wondering when they may repair the difficulty that has arisen. Afterwards they draw their conclusions and will make good provision, please God, and will gather together often and enjoy themselves at their ease; but the goodman to whom the outrage was done, shall pay for all.

After they have decided how they shall proceed, they make merry and jest among themselves. One of them says to the daughter:

" I would not have as bad a night as your husband will have this night."

Another will say: " Would that I knew what he is doing at this moment and that I might see his face."

" *Par Dieu.*" says another. " When you heard about such an one and me (whom my husband accused me of and I defended myself well, thank God!), for more than three months my husband could neither eat nor sleep. And when he was in bed, he turned and twisted from one side to the other and kept sighing; and, by my faith, I laughed to myself between the sheets and stuffed the sheet into my mouth."

" Alack," says the other, " the poor man who fled is now in great sorrow."

" Alack, my dear," says the mother, " the wicked fellow could not keep from appearing twice today in front of this house; but I ordered him not to come again."

And the serving-wench says:

" By my troth, I found him just now in front of the fountain. He gave me a huge pie to bring to you and said that tomorrow morning he will send you a pastry; and he sends you and the company so many greetings it is a marvel."

" Alas," says one of the gossips, " upon my word, tis a great pity."

"Verily," says the other, "we shall eat the pie for his sake ere we go home."

"And by Our Holy Mother Mary," says another, "I would he were here."

"So help me!" says the serving-wench, "how pleased he would be! For he is all atremble and so pale he looks as if he were dead!"

"Faith, my gossip, shall we go and ask him to come?"

"Willingly," says the mother, "but let him enter through the back."

Then perhaps he comes and they chaff and banter and enjoy themselves and they take pity on him and make room for him. Then they send for the goodman's serving-wench, who knows all and knew everything that went before, and perhaps had a fine new gown out of it. The serving-wench comes and one of the gossips asks her:

"Now swear by our Lord Jesus Christ! How does your master look?"

"How he looks?" says she. "Do not ask. For, on my soul, ever since yesterday morning when the terrible thing happened, he has neither drunk nor eaten nor slept. By my faith, he sat down at table this morning, but he did not touch a mouthful; for when he had put a piece of meat in his mouth, he could not swallow it and spat it out. And then he leaned over the table and was sad; and he is as pale and changed as a dead man. Then he picks up his knife, with which he cuts, and bangs on the table; then he goes into the garden; then he comes back and cannot stand still or keep himself in countenance; and all day and all night long he is convulsed with sobs; there is no man who would not pity him."

"Pity!" says the other. "He will get over it, so God pleases. *Par Dieu*, my gossip, you have seen many another just as ill who has been well cured, thank God. But verily," says she to the serving-wench, "it is largely your fault. Well do you know the facts and your mistress trusted you. Why did you not protect her?"

"Aha! By the holy saints! I never told him to come at that hour, for never once have I

seen him play the trick he did, may God curse him!"

"Amen," they all say; and so be it.

Thus they banter and cackle and make mock of the goodman. Then they confer as to which one shall go first to speak to the goodman who sits in his own home like a man sentenced to be hanged. And first come one or two of his favourite gossips whom he likes to see. And one of them speaks to him from the threshold.

"What are you doing, my goodman?"

And he makes no reply and lets them come up to him. They come in and sit down very close to him. And one of them says:

"How do you feel, my goodman?"

"I do not feel anything," says he. "What does that mean?"

"Verily," says she. "I must scold you, for my gossip, the mother of your wife, told me I know not what folly. And on my word of honour you are mad to believe such nonsense. For, by the soul that beats in my breast, I am as certain as I am of death and will swear on all the holy saints that she has never done any wrong nor had any wish to do so."

And the other gossip tells him:

" By Our Lady of Puy, I have known her since childhood and she is the best girl there is in all the country. But it is a great pity that ever she was given to you; for you have defamed her and without cause, and you will never be able to make amends."

" On my word," says the serving-wench, " my dear ladies and friends, I know not what my master has thought or discovered; but never in my life did I see any folly in my lady and I have served her very faithfully; and it would be indeed strange had I not known it."

" By God," says the goodman, " I saw her with my own eyes! "

" Faith," says one of the gossips, " you did not, no matter what you say; for just because people are close to each other there is no reason to think there is harm in it."

" Well do I know," says the serving-wench, " that the rascal would have liked it well enough;

but there is no man in the world to whom my lady wishes more harm than to him. And I do not know how he entered the house for, I swear by my hopes of Paradise, he has never been here before and Madam would rather he were hanged on the gallows and that she were burned at the stake. I have served you faithfully four years, poor as I am; but I will swear on the holy relics of this city that Madam has been as good and honest wife to you as ever wife was. Ha! Think it not! How could I not have known," says she, "if there had been any wrongdoing? And, by my word, I was close enough at hand. Please God I might be as easily absolved of all the sins I have ever committed as she is of this one, though no man has ever touched my lips but he whom I married, God keep his soul. I fear no man alive."

Then come the other gossips, one after the other, and there is not one who does not offer excellent reasons. One says:

"I swear by the holy saints, my goodman, I think I am the one woman in the world who loves you most, next to your wife. But I swear to you on my word of honour that had I seen evil in her, I would tell you."

"Upon my word," says the other, "it was the devil's own doing to separate you because he could not harm you otherwise."

"Alas!" says another, "The poor girl never stops weeping."

"*Par Dieu*," says another, "She is on the way to dying."

"And do you think," says a third, "that we are so foolish that, if she were as you say, we would suffer her in our company? Faith," says she, "no, indeed, we are not such fools that we would deign to speak to her, nor would we suffer her to remain on our street or near us."

The mother comes weeping and runs to him and pretends that she would scratch out his eyes and says:

"Ha! Cursed be the hour that ever she was given to you, for you have destroyed her honour and mine! Alas," says she, "we did you great honour to give her to you, for if she had so desired she could have been wed to a noble knight; whereby she would now be in great honour. But she would have none but you. That is the reason she is so unhappy; it is indeed a misfortune that has befallen her! "

" Ha, may gossip," says one of the other gossips, " Do not be so angry! "

" Ha, my dear friends," says she, " If my daughter had done wrong, I would not care, for I myself would have strangled her. But do you think I like to see my daughter thus put to shame without cause, and for such great wrong that may never be amended? "

Then they all begin to scold and blame him. And the poor man begins to ponder and does not know what to do; but in truth, he gets over it in the end and is consoled. The mother goes away and her gossips soothe him gently and say it is no wonder the mother is angry; and they promise to bring back the daughter and so take their leave.

Afterwards comes a Dominican or a Franciscan friar who is his confessor, and his wife's also, and he knows the whole farrago and receives a present every year to absolve her of all her sins and he comes to the husband and says:

"I marvel greatly at what I am told. *Certes*, I must reproach you, for I swear by my lord, Saint Dominic or by my lord, Saint Augustin, I have known your wife for more than ten years, but I swear on my hope of salvation that she is one of the best women in all the land; and I know her well for she is my daughter in confession and I have questioned her thoroughly. But never have I found aught but all the good that may be in woman, nor was her body ever sullied by mortal sin, and on that I pledge my soul."

Thus is the goodman subdued and greatly repents of having created such an uproar and believes that there was never anything. Now we must learn what profit the goodman will gain from having caused such a disturbance; henceforth he will be more downtrodden than ever and perhaps he will become a craven. For his wife, whom he has defamed, will have no shame since well she knows that all have heard the story and she will stop at nothing. And perhaps the mother, the gossips, the cousins, the neighbours (some of whom had not known of the affair) will be in league with the wife and will help her to have her little frolics as they helped her to bridle her husband because he was too loudmouthed. And the gallant, for his part, will do much service and give them many pastries and tarts which they will eat together; and the husband must pay for all and never will hear a word of it, for the gossips will see to that. For never would he believe they would consent to such frolics and he will no longer be suspicious. His resources will be squandered to support this farrago. The serving-wench, who well knows all that goes on and who has laboured sore to make peace, will be as great a lady as her mistress and will have her lovers to visit her and her mistress will help her, for one good turn deserves another.

Now is the goodman caught in the trap; and do what he may, for whatever cheer she makes him, she will never love him. He will grow old and fall into penury according to the rules of the game. Thus will he waste his life in torments, suffering and groans and there he will remain always and will end his days in misery.

CONCLUSION

Here end the fifteen joys of marriage, which I call joys because they who are married can have no knowledge of the matters above-mentioned but consider them great happiness, or so it appears, because for nothing in the world would they have them otherwise. But, as for me, I hold such things to be the greatest misfortunes that may be on earth. And if women complain that I have not attributed or assigned the said matters, which I consider misfortunes, to them as well as to men, they will forgive me — if it please them — though I have said nothing in their disfavor for it is all in their praise and honour.

Moreover, as a general rule, the things above-mentioned befall men, as I have said; and I do not say, nor would I say, that all those joys, or even two or three of them, come to every husband; but I can say for certain that there is no married man, however discreet, prudent or wily he may be, who does not have at least one of those joys or several of them. Wherefore we may well conclude that the man who deliberately puts himself into such servitude, does so of his own free will.

However I would not say that it is not well to marry. But I do not hold such follies to be joys or felicities. At least men should take heed not to allow themselves to become debased by it; for each sees what befalls the others and they are quick to mock and play jokes on them. But when they marry, they are more debased than the others. Thus every man must take heed not to mock others, for I see none of them exempt from the joys above—mentioned. But each man, in his own heart, believes the contrary and thinks that he is protected and fortunate above others; and he who believes it most, is the most bridled. I know not what it is, except it be the luck of the game.

And if I am asked if any remedy might be devised, my answer is that this is possible, difficult though it may be; but at least there is a remedy, though for the present, I shall say no more. But were anyone to ask me by word of mouth, I would give him my opinion; though for the present I keep silent that no lady, demoiselle or other woman may take it ill of me. Though, as I have said in good faith, all is in praise of women; and he who understands what I have written here will find that men have ever the worst part, which is an honour to women. And I have written it at the request of certain demoiselles who urged me to do so. And if they are not satisfied and would have me take the trouble to write for them, on their behalf and against men, I offer myself in good faith. For therein have I better material than this, seeing the great wrongs, griefs and oppressions men do unto women in divers places, generally by brute force and for no reason. For women are naturally weak and defenceless and are always ready to obey and to serve, without which men could not, nor might not, live.